Evolution EXPOSED

Earth Science

ROGER PATTERSON

1:1
answersingenesis
Hebron, Kentucky
United States of America

On the Cover: The cover photo shows the three actual textbooks reviewed, with yellow flags on each page containing evolutionary concepts.

First printing: July 2008

ISBN: 1-60092-191-4

Cover design: Brandie Lucas
Interior layout: Diane King
Editors: Lori Jaworski, Stacia McKeever, Gary Vaterlaus

Printed in the United States of America.

This book is dedicated to my wonderful wife who has supported me in my work and walk and who teaches my children godliness in a world drowning in godlessness.

> And the LORD God said, "It is not good that man should be alone; I will make him a helper comparable to him." –Genesis 2:18

I would also like to thank Dr. Jason Lisle, Dr. Georgia Purdom, and Dr. Andrew Snelling for their work in reviewing the content of this book, as well as the editors, reviewers, and illustrators who work hard behind the scenes.

> Without counsel, plans go awry, But in the multitude of counselors they are established. –Proverbs 15:22

Roger Patterson earned his B.S. Ed. degree in biology with a minor in chemistry from Montana State University–Billings. Before joining the curriculum development team at Answers in Genesis, he taught biology and chemistry for eight years in Wyoming's public school system and assisted the Wyoming Department of Education in developing assessments and standards for children in public schools.

TABLE OF CONTENTS

INTRODUCTION

The purpose of this book is to provide students and teachers in earth science and space science classrooms with biblical and scientific insight into the true nature of evolution, uniformitarian geology, and the big bang as they are taught in public schools. Answers in Genesis (AiG) has long suggested that students are being indoctrinated with evolutionary ideas in the public schools. This reference book provides evidence to support that claim in the earth science textbooks.

After reviewing three of the most commonly used high school earth science textbooks, we again found an astounding number of references to evolutionary, old-earth, and big bang ideas. Virtually every chapter in the reviewed books contains implied or explicit references to these ideas.

For the sake of discussion in this book, the terms *evolutionist* and *evolutionary* will be used to refer to those people and ideas that rely on an old earth and universe. There are Christians who reject the biological evolution of life on earth but accept the evolution of the universe and the earth from the big bang based on the "scientific evidence." This position is problematic because it accepts naturalistic explanations for the formation of the universe and the earth but rejects them in the case of biologic change. That makes this view, commonly referred to as progressive creationism, logically inconsistent as well as contrary to the clear teaching of Scripture. The term *evolution* is commonly defined in the textbooks as change over time. So, the development of the universe can be referred to as cosmic evolution, and the development of the earth can be referred to as geologic evolution.

A similar idea, often called theistic evolution or old-earth creationism, suggests that God used the big bang to form the universe 15 billion years ago. Life on earth was then set in motion by God and biological evolution ran its course to produce all of the life, present and past, on the earth. Exactly how humans came to be is debated amongst proponents of these ideas, but the plain reading of the Creation account in Genesis is rejected. All of these ideas start with man's understanding of the universe and attempt to fit the Bible into that understanding. This leads to many compromises and an inconsistent interpretation of Scripture. For more on these evolutionary positions I would encourage you to visit www.answersingenesis.org/go/compromise.

The biblical, antievolutionary position is known as young-earth creationism and starts with the Bible's account of the origin of the earth and universe as the authority. This is the position that is argued for in this book. Starting with God's eyewitness account of the creation of the universe we can then use scientific principles to understand the world around us. From the Bible we can conclude that the earth is about 6,000 years old, man lived with dinosaurs, there was a worldwide Flood, and God came to earth as Jesus Christ to die for our sins. Using these ideas as a framework for scientific exploration, we can begin to understand how the world around us came to be in the state that it is in. This is not an unscientific position, as many would claim, but a God-honoring approach to studying the creation.

This book is intended to be a reference that students can take into the classroom. Each chapter opens with a summary of the differences between the evolutionary (including the geologic time scale and big bang cosmology) and creationist interpretations of the chapter topic. The summary is followed by a table of the evolutionary concepts presented in the textbooks and their respective page numbers. A more thorough discussion of the topic follows the table of references. Each concept is linked to articles that present a creationist interpretation of the evidence. The articles have been summarized for your convenience. Students are encouraged to read the full articles, using the provided URLs, before using the information to challenge the textbook's claims. The articles are referenced by two numbers separated by a colon. For example, article 2:5 is found in Chapter 2 and is the fifth article in the list. Complete citations for the articles are found in an index at the back of the book.

The next section contains questions that students can ask teachers concerning the ideas presented in class. Students are encouraged to ask the questions in a Christ-like manner (see the section below on Respectful Questioning). These questions are general in nature and can be modified to reflect the specific examples used in class. Following the questions is a list of books and other resources.

The indexes and tables throughout the book can be used by anyone, regardless of whether you use the textbooks that were reviewed.

The three textbooks cited in this book often give different dates and hypotheses. When the dates disagree, the oldest date is generally given. In some cases, the hypotheses contradict one another. The statements used in the tables are intended to be generalizations, not extensive descriptions. The use of dates of millions of years and the use of common evolutionary terms is for the sake of discussion and in no way should be taken to mean that we agree with their validity.

Using the References and Companion Website

We have made every attempt to make the reference materials accessible to everyone. Whenever possible, the reference articles and chapters are available on the internet. This book also features a companion website (www.evolutionexposed.com) that can be used to link to the reference materials. The website allows you to access the most current information and will provide updates that will equip you in defending your faith. You can also use the website to access other helpful products, such as DVDs, witnessing tracts, and books.

We have chosen to use a variety of sources for the references in this book. When information from groups other than Answers in Genesis is used, articles have been selectively chosen to represent views consistent with AiG's mission and statement of faith. The websites themselves may contain material that is not necessarily endorsed by AiG.

Many organizations around the world are dedicated to upholding biblical authority and promoting that authority by addressing the creation/evolution debate. A wide variety of materials and information is available through this network of organizations. There very well may be a creation group in your local area or state. Becoming a member of one of these groups is a great way to stay connected with current issues and become equipped to engage in the culture war and advance the gospel.

> And who is he who will harm you if you become followers of what is good? But even if you should suffer for righteousness' sake, you are blessed. "And do not be afraid of their threats, nor be troubled."

Peter continues with a challenge in verses 15–16:

> But sanctify the Lord God in your hearts, and always be ready to give a defense to everyone who asks you a reason for the hope that is in you, with meekness and fear; having a good conscience, that when they defame you as evildoers, those who revile your good conduct in Christ may be ashamed.

This passage tells us that we need to set apart Christ in our hearts, study to be prepared to give an answer, and speak the truth with gentleness and respect. We are in a battle, and the stakes are high. Even if a classmate or teacher does not come to Christ, you may be planting seeds that will sprout some day.

It should encourage you to know that a wealth of information is available from many sources to help you defend your faith. Below is a list of books which contain the type of information that will be helpful. These books include secular and creation scientists who challenge the idea of Darwinian evolution, uniformitarian geology, and big bang cosmology from both scientific and religious perspectives. There is also a huge collection of articles, some of which are summarized in the following chapters, available at www.answersingenesis.org. New articles are posted daily; so keep checking the website for the most current information regarding the creation/evolution controversy. Magazines and newsletters are another source of current information available from AiG. Many DVDs and witnessing tracts are available for you to share. The most effective changes start at the grass roots level, and you can be a powerful tool within the public school system to defend the authority of the Bible from the very first verse.

It is important that students realize they have more rights in the classroom than they might think. Whenever assignments are given, the student has the right to express his thoughts and beliefs through those assignments. For example, a report on a famous scientist might include how that scientist's faith in God or belief in the Bible influenced his career or research. Religious topics may be used whenever students are allowed to determine the content of the essay, homework, artwork, and so on. For more information on student rights in public schools visit www.answersingenesis.org/go/student-rights.

When answering questions from the textbook or teacher, students are often expected to provide answers that assume evolutionary ideas are true. In such cases, the student may want to preface the question with a disclaimer. The disclaimer might say, "According to the textbook . . ." or "As the idea was presented in class . . . ." This will communicate to the teacher that the student has learned the concepts presented in the class but that she does not necessarily agree with them. When appropriate, the student may also consider adding her personal beliefs or the biblical interpretation after she has answered the question from an evolutionary perspective. This approach will allow her to meet the academic requirements of the classroom setting and also express her belief that the interpretation presented by the textbook or curriculum is false.

Textbooks Reviewed

To develop this resource, three of the most popular high school earth science textbooks were chosen. The publisher and page number are provided for photos, figures, or tables (e.g., Glencoe 327). The full citations for the textbooks are listed below.

F. S. Hess et al., *Earth Science: Geology, the Environment, and the Universe* (Teacher Wraparound Edition), (New York: Glencoe/McGraw Hill, 2005).

This text will be referred to as Glencoe throughout this book.

E. Tarbuck, F. K. Lutgens, *Earth Science* (Indiana Teacher's Edition), (Upper Saddle River, NJ: Pearson Prentice Hall, 2006).

This text will be referred to as Prentice Hall throughout this book.

M. A. Allison, A. T. DeGaetano, and J. M. Pasachoff, *Earth Science* (Teacher Edition), (Austin, TX: Holt, Rinehart, and Winston, 2006).

This text will be referred to as Holt throughout this book.

Tools for Digging Deeper

The Biblical Basis for Modern Science by Henry Morris (semi-technical), Master Books, 2002.

A comprehensive resource for the serious student of creation. Gives in-depth information on the creation/evolution issue in biology, geology, astronomy, the history of the nations, etc.

Bones of Contention by Marvin Lubenow (semi-technical), Baker Books, 2004.

Professor Lubenow examines the fossil evidence for human evolution and exposes the philosophical and scientific untruths. Each of the alleged ancestors is examined and shown to be an evolutionary farce. The myth of human evolution is thoroughly dismantled in this book.

Creation: Facts of Life by Gary Parker, Master Books, 2006.

In *Creation: Facts of Life*, Dr. Parker respectfully describes the evidences he once used to preach evolution, but then he explains how the rest of the evidence points away from evolution and toward a perfect world created by God, ruined by man, restored to new life in Christ. This classic has been updated and expanded into a powerful and layman-friendly format, filled with many of the latest findings in science.

Darwin on Trial by Phillip Johnson, InterVarsity Press, 1993.

Professor Johnson uses his incisive legal mind to demonstrate that Darwinian evolution is based not on fact, but on faith. Johnson examines the evidence used to support evolution and its naturalistic philosophy, and he declares a mistrial.

Darwin's Black Box by Michael Behe (semi-technical), Free Press, 1996.

Biochemistry professor Michael Behe uses the concept of irreducible complexity to demonstrate how Darwinian evolution fails to provide a mechanism for building systems that work as intact units. Behe does not endorse a young earth, but his critique of evolutionary theory from within the scientific establishment demonstrates the shaky ground that the philosophy is based on.

Evolution: A Theory in Crisis by Michael Denton, Adler & Adler, 1986.

This book by a noncreationist is hard-hitting, factual, and objective. It does not argue in favor of creation, but is a clear, balanced, responsible, and scientifically accurate account of the ever-growing crisis in evolutionary circles.

Evolution: The Fossils Still Say No! by Duane Gish, Master Books, 1995.

The most compelling critique available anywhere of the supposedly key argument for evolution: the fossil record. Dr. Gish documents, from the writings of evolutionists, the complete absence of true evolutionary transitional forms.

Evolution Exposed: Biology by Roger Patterson, Answers in Genesis, 2006.

This book helps teens to discern the chronic bias toward belief in evolution that permeates today's four most popular high school biology textbooks. Virtually every chapter in each of the secular textbooks contains implied or explicit references to evolutionary beliefs, which are misrepresented as irrefutable facts. However, in *Evolution Exposed: Biology* these misrepresentations are cross-referenced with online articles and publications that provide both scientific and biblical answers. Key terms are defined, articles are summarized and false ideas are refuted. *Evolution Exposed: Biology* is thoroughly indexed by topic so anyone can use it as a reference. Christian students are equipped and inspired to recognize and respectfully challenge evolutionary indoctrination (in class, research papers, and normal interactions outside of school). Using tables, web links, charts and illustrations, documented facts that counter evolutionary teaching in a powerful and organized fashion are synchronized with each textbook's sequence.

Exploring Planet Earth by John Hudson Tiner, Master Books, 1997.

The first in a series of books on science, geared toward the homeschool family. With definitions of terms and identification of explorers, scientists, etc., this book gives students excellent introductory knowledge of famous people and history.

Footprints in the Ash by John Morris and Steven Austin, Master Books, 2003.

This lavishly illustrated, full-color "picture book" shares the entire explosive story of Mount St. Helens. Written by two experts who know the volcano—and its famous 1980 eruption—best. Includes rare photographs by the authors. A powerful testament to the Creator and Judge, who forms canyons in just hours, not millions of years!

The Fossil Book by Gary Parker, Master Books, 2006.

This book uncovers the exciting story of fossils—how they formed, where they are found, and how to build your own collection—all from a creationist's perspective. Fascinating, informative, and filled with color photos and illustrations.

Frozen in Time by Michael Oard, Master Books, 2004.

Meteorologist Michael Oard gives plausible explanations of the seemingly unsolvable mysteries about the Ice Age and the woolly mammoths. Many other related topics are explained, including super floods, ice cores, man in the Ice Age, and the number of ice ages.

The Geology Book by John Morris, Master Books, 2000.

Dr. Morris explains the formation and study of rocks in a clear, understandable way. The layers of rock were supposedly laid down over the billions of years of earth's history. Morris demonstrates that the rocks tell the story of creation and the catastrophe of a global Flood only a few thousand years ago.

Grand Canyon: A Different View by Tom Vail, Master Books, 2003.

Whether gaping down the huge chasm from the rim, or navigating the Colorado River below, visitors to the Grand Canyon see a perspective that words can't describe. In fact, perspective is the message of this wonderful story from nature. Visit this marvelous site yourself, through the photographs and essays in this book, and think about your own perspective.

Grand Canyon: Monument to Catastrophe by Steven Austin (technical), Institute for Creation Research, 1994.

Eminent geologist Dr. Steven Austin explains from a biblical standpoint how the Grand Canyon was formed. This book contains a wealth of information about geology and biology that equips Christians to defend Genesis, the young earth position, the worldwide Flood, etc. Also includes material on the eruption of Mount St. Helens.

An Ice Age Caused by the Genesis Flood by Michael Oard (technical), Institute for Creation Research, 2002.

A detailed study of the scientific evidence that the Ice Age was caused by the Flood of Noah, and that it occurred thoroughly in accord with the biblical chronology of a recent creation. Fully documented from secular sources.

The Lie: Evolution by Ken Ham, Master Books, 1998.

Ken Ham is best known for his message on the relevance of creation and the importance of Genesis. Humorous and easy-to-read, this book powerfully equips Christians to defend the book of Genesis and opens eyes to the harmful effects of evolution on today's society.

The Missoula Flood Controversy by Michael Oard (technical), Institute for Creation Research, 2004.

Do evolutionists really ignore significant scientific evidence that supports biblical history? In this in-depth analysis of J Harland Bretz's controversial study in the 1920s on the proposed Missoula Flood in the state of

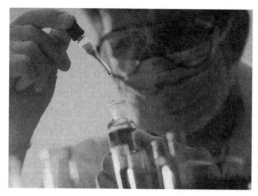

The examples of science used in the textbooks show only operational (observational) science. This type of science, which makes observations and repeats experiments in the present, allows us to produce technology that benefits mankind. Evolution does not fit within the definition of operational science and should be classified as historical (origins) science.

Operational (Observational) Science: a systematic approach to understanding that uses observable, testable, repeatable, and falsifiable experimentation to understand how nature commonly behaves.

Operational science is the type of science that allows us to understand how DNA codes for proteins in cells. It is the type of science that has allowed us to cure and treat diseases, put a man on the moon, build satellites and telescopes, and make products that are useful to humans. Biblical creationists believe that God has created a universe that uses a set of natural laws that operate consistently in the universe. Understanding how those laws operate is the basis for scientific thinking.

Laws of nature are descriptions of the way God normally upholds the universe. But God is not bound by these laws. He is free to act in other ways in order to accomplish an unusual and extraordinary purpose. So, miracles are possible within the Christian worldview. Naturalistic scientists simply dismiss the possibility of the supernatural. They do this not for logical reasons, but because miracles are incompatible with their beliefs. But then again, they have no good reason to think that laws of nature should exist in the first place. The Christian can make sense of both science and miracles. The naturalist cannot account for either.

Historical (Origins) Science: interpreting evidence from past events based on a presupposed philosophical point of view.

The past is not directly observable, testable, repeatable, or falsifiable; so interpretations of past events present greater challenges than interpretations involving operational science. Neither creation nor evolution is directly observable, testable, repeatable, or falsifiable. Each is based on certain philosophical assumptions about how the earth began. Naturalistic evolution assumes that there was no God, and biblical creation assumes that there was a God who created everything in the universe. Starting from two opposite presuppositions and looking at the same facts, the explanations of the history of the universe are very different. The argument is not over the facts—the facts are the same—it is over the way the facts should be interpreted.

Evolutionists often claim that people misuse the word *theory* when discussing science and don't make a distinction between a scientific theory and the common use of the word *theory*. You may say, "I have a theory about why Mr. Jones's hair looks funny" but that theory has never been compared to a broad set of observations. This is not the sense of a theory in science.

In light of this, few would argue that there are different types of theories. So it would be good to refine this term further to avoid any baiting and switching of the word *theory*. Just as it was valuable to distinguish between operational and historical science, it would be good to do the same with operational and historical theories.

Operational Theory: an explanation of a set of facts based on a broad set of repeatable and testable observations that is generally accepted within a group of scientists.

That evolution has been elevated to the status of an operational theory (and *fact* in the opinion of some) is not due to the strength of the evidence, but in spite of it. Because evolutionary ideas are interpretations of past events, they are not as well-founded as testable scientific theories like Einstein's theory of relativity. These theories offer predictable models and the ability to conduct experiments to determine their validity in different circumstances. Molecules-to-man evolution does not offer this opportunity because these events happened in the past. Therefore, evolution is not an operational theory. For these reasons, evolution could be considered an historical theory, along with creation models and other origins theories.

It is important to recognize that people's presuppositions influence the way they interpret the facts. Evolution is based on a reasoning process that rejects God. Creation starts from the authority of God's Word. Your presuppositions are like a pair of glasses that you wear to look at the world around you.

Historical Theory: an explanation of past events based on the interpretation of evidence that is available in the present.

Evolution, whether cosmic, biological, or geological, fits this definition of theory, but it relies on the assumption of naturalism. In the naturalistic scientific community, evolution has become a theory that is assumed to be an established fact and not an explanation. Evolution is the prevailing paradigm, and most scientists have stopped questioning the underlying assumptions that the theory is based upon. Creation scientists develop theories, too, in light of biblical truth, but they are not as widely accepted by scientists. All interpretations (theories) of the past are based on assumptions and cannot be equated with facts that are observable in the present. This holds true for creationist or evolutionist theories. (See article 1:3 on page 31 for more on this topic.)

Evolution also relies heavily on the assumption of uniformitarianism—a belief that the present is the key to the past. According to uniformitarians, the processes in the universe have been occurring at a relatively constant rate. One of these processes is the rate of rock formation and erosion. If rocks form or erode at a certain rate in the present, uniformitarians believe that they must have always formed or eroded at nearly the same rate. This assumption is accepted even though there are no observations of the rate of erosion from the distant past and there is no way to empirically test the erosion rate of the past. However, the Bible makes it very clear that some events of the past were radically different from those we commonly observe today. Noah's Flood, for example, would have devastated the face of the earth and created a landscape of billions of dead things buried in layers of rock, which is exactly what we see.

Just as evolutionists weren't there to see evolution happen over several billion years, neither were creationists there to see the events of the six days of creation. The difference is that creationists have the Creator's eyewitness account of the events of creation, while evolutionists must create a story to explain origins without the supernatural. Many scientists believe the story, but that does not make the story true. Believing the Bible and the information that has been revealed to us by our Creator gives us a foundation for thinking—including our thinking about science. Good operational science can provide us with answers to many questions about the world around us and how it operates, but it cannot answer the questions of where we came from and why we are here. Those questions are outside the scope of operational science. But we are not left without an answer. God has given us the answers to those questions in His Word, the Bible.

Reference Article Summaries

1:1 The nature of science and of theories on origins, Gish, www.icr.org/article/391

Scientific theories must be testable and capable of being proven false. Neither evolution nor biblical creation qualifies as a scientific theory in this sense, because each deals with historical events that cannot be repeated. Both evo-

Making observations about canyons and planets can increase understanding about many aspects of geology and astronomy. But it is important to recognize the limitations when you cross into historical science.

lution and creation are based on unobserved assumptions about past events. It is inconsistent to say that evolution qualifies as a scientific theory while creation does not. Both have scientific character by attempting to correlate scientific data within a certain framework (model).

No theory of origins can avoid using philosophical statements as a foundation. Creationists use a supernatural act by an Intelligent Designer to explain the origin of the universe and the life we see on earth. Evolutionists do not allow any supernatural explanation as a foundation but insist that only natural laws and processes can be used as explanations. Both are worldviews used to interpret the data. The data is the same; the interpretations arrive at different conclusions based on the starting assumptions. Allowing only evolutionary teaching in public schools promotes an atheistic worldview, just as much as teaching only creation would promote a theistic worldview. Students are indoctrinated to believe they are meaningless products of evolution and that no God exists to whom they are accountable. Life on earth was either created or it developed in some progressive manner; there are no other alternatives. While there are many versions of both creation and evolution, both cannot be true.

1:2 Feedback: a "more glorious" means for creation? Hodge, www.answersingenesis.org/go/glorious

Accepting that God created the universe in the way that He said He did is a common stumbling block for many who want to accept the interpretation promoted by evolutionary scientists. There are many reasons why the God of the Bible would not have used evolution and the big bang to create the universe. Those who hold to these theories are putting man's fallible interpretations of scientific data into the text of Genesis.

Accepting the big bang or evolution as factual accounts of the origin of life and the universe is not scientific. They are interpretations of facts. The assumptions that underlie the interpretations are based on the idea that man can determine truth independent of God. Operational science is based on repeatable observations and falsifiable statements, while historical science is based on interpreting data that cannot be repeated. Operational science leads to computers and space shuttles as products of repeatable processes. Historical science leads to shifting interpretations that are not reliable.

The only way to arrive at a true interpretation is to start with true assumptions. Since the Bible is the eyewitness account of the Creator of the universe, it is the best starting point for interpreting past events.

1:3 Creation: where's the proof? Ham, www.answersingenesis. org/go/proof

All scientists, creationist or evolutionist, have the same evidence; the difference is the presuppositions that are used to interpret that evidence. All reasoning is based on presuppositions. Biblical creationists start with the assumption that the Bible provides an accurate eyewitness history of

It is not true to say that there is different evidence for creation and evolution. Everyone has the same evidence—it is just interpreted in different ways.

the universe as a basis for scientific thought. Evolutionists begin with the presupposition that only natural laws can be used to explain the facts. Facts exist in the present, and our interpretations are an attempt to connect the past to the present. The evolutionists must assume everything about the past, while biblical creationists have the Bible as a "time machine" that can provide valuable insight into the past.

If someone expects you to argue that the Bible or creation is true without using the Bible as evidence, they are stacking the deck in their favor. They are insisting that facts are neutral and that truth can be determined independent of God. Facts are always interpreted, and the Word of God is absolutely trustworthy. Demonstrating how the Bible can be used to effectively explain a fact, like the presence of fossils, demonstrates that it is valid as a filter for interpreting facts. Many people do not realize how their presuppositions impact their thinking. Exposing a person's presuppositions will help them to see how they filter the facts; challenging the origin of those presuppositions will force them to evaluate their stance.

If science depends on naturalistic explanations, it must accept that our thoughts are simply the products of chemical reactions that evolved from random chance. How can you ultimately rely on randomness to evolve the correct way of thinking? If there is no God, how can one talk about reality? How can one even rationally believe that there is such a thing as truth, let alone decide what it is?

1:4 God & Natural Law, Lisle, www.answersingenesis.org/articles/am/v1/n2/God-natural-law

The universe is governed by laws that everything must obey. These laws describe the way God normally accomplishes His will in the universe. If the universe were a product of a random big bang would we expect to see orderly principles operating throughout the universe? The laws of nature exist only because God wills them to be so. Atheists cannot explain this order since they reject the existence of a Lawgiver.

Observational science shows us that living things can only come from other living things. Evolutionists must reject this law and believe that life can arise spontaneously from nonliving chemicals. These nonliving chemicals also follow certain laws. The laws of chemistry determine the properties of each atom and how those atoms bond to form compounds and molecules. Quantum physics is responsible for the order seen in the periodic table. If the laws of quantum physics were slightly different, atoms might not be possible. God designed the laws of physics so that the laws of chemistry would be correct and life would be possible.

Based on observations, Kepler was able to determine that the planets follow predictable orbits. In a random universe this would not be possible. The laws of planetary motion are also based on the laws of gravity and motion that were formulated by another creationist, Isaac Newton. The fundamental laws of physics exist only because God wills them to.

Mathematics and logic are abstract in nature and would be the same regardless of the type of universe that God created. The atheist cannot explain the origin of these laws, but he will borrow them to support his own worldview. The atheist must accept the laws of mathematics and logic but he rejects the Creator whose nature they reflect. The fact that these laws are uniform throughout the universe is one of the foundational principles of science. Secular scientists have no reason to believe that these laws should be constant. Since we know that God created this order and that He does not change we are not surprised that He has chosen to uphold the universe in a consistent way. Thus the Christian can explain the consistency of the natural laws.

1:5 Human-caused global warming slight so far, Oard, www. answersingenesis.org/articles/am/v1/n2/human-caused-global-warming

There has been much made of the effects of human activity on the earth's atmosphere, specifically concerning global warming. Some scientists claim that the impact of global warming will cause either a global ice age or melt all of the ice causing sea levels to rise. There are many scientists who believe that the claims are premature and that there is not enough evidence to say that the current trend is not just a part of a climate cycle.

But what should Christians think about the global warming issue? Many of those involved are antagonistic to the Christian worldview and are intentionally distorting the issue. Use of interpretations based on uniformitarian assumptions to support claims should not be accepted as legitimate. Many of these interpretations are built on the assumption that ice cores give us data from hundreds of thousands of years of earth history. Others are motivated by the profits from stirring the political pot and blaming the problems on oil companies.

It does appear that there has been a small increase in global surface temperature and carbon dioxide levels in the recent past. While carbon dioxide does act as a greenhouse gas, water vapor is much more important and acts to regulate the earth's temperature. Interpreting how much impact man can have on global warming is difficult. Scientists are uncertain about how much of the warming is from natural cycles and how much is from man-made sources.

Using computer models, it is not clear how much impact an increase in carbon dioxide levels will have. Even if the impact could be known, there is still debate about how much benefit or harm will come from global warming. There would be many benefits to weigh against the negative aspects, and these benefits are not publicized in the media.

Ultimately, there must be more research done to understand the global warming trend and whether it will result in positive or negative impacts on humanity. If the evidence shows that global warming should be reduced, we should find and invest in new, cost-effective technologies to do so.

1:6 Creation and the flat earth, Faulkner, www.creationresearch. org/creation_matters/97/cm9711.html

Creationists are often ridiculed for believing in something akin to a flat earth. However, there is no reason to believe that the ancients actually believed in a flat earth, and the Bible does not teach that the earth is flat.

The ancients knew that the shadow of the earth during a lunar eclipse was curved regardless of when the eclipse occurred. The only shape that could accomplish this is a sphere. The orientation of the North Star and the visibility of different constellations as you move south also indicate a spherical earth. It can be determined that the moon is a sphere from simple observation over time, so some may have concluded that the earth is spherical by analogy.

The size of the earth was calculated by Eratosthenes using the length of shadows during the summer solstice, and it was quite accurate when compared to today's value. This information on the shape of the earth was adopted into the thinking of the church and would have been understood at the time of Columbus. Because Columbus sailed only a short distance, he could not have proved the world was round, far short of circumnavigating the globe.

The myth that Columbus was sailing on a flat earth was perpetuated by a fictional account found in a story by Washington Irving. This idea is explained in the book *Inventing the Flat Earth*. The notion of Columbus's crew believing they would fall off of the edge of the earth is a popular, but false, idea.

Questions to Consider

- Do all scientists believe in naturalistic (cosmic, biological, chemical, geologic) evolution? Why or why not?

- There are two contenders for the history of the universe and life on earth: some form of naturalism (evolution) or supernatural creation. Are there really any alternatives to some form of naturalistic evolution in science if science is restricted to naturalism?

- Since evolution and creation are both based on religious beliefs (basic presuppositions), why should one and not the other be taught as science in public schools?

- Should there be a distinction between experimental (operational) science and historical (origins) science?

- Since a naturalistic approach to science can only refer to materialistic explanations, how can naturalists use logic if logic is not a material part of the universe?

- Is it necessary for science to allow only naturalism?

- Would all scientific thought and advancement end if supernatural creation was accepted as a possible model for how the universe and life on earth began?

- Why is supernatural creation considered to be a "science stopper" and not a "science starter," considering that most of the founding fathers of science believed in the Bible and a supernatural creation event?

- If an all-knowing Creator God exists, wouldn't it be logical to say that He knows about the scientific laws He created? Why not use what He says as a foundation for scientific thinking?

Tools for Digging Deeper

(see a complete list in the Introduction)

The Biblical Basis for Modern Science by Henry Morris

Creation: Facts of Life by Gary Parker

Creation Scientists Answer Their Critics by Duane Gish

Darwin on Trial by Phillip Johnson

Darwin's Black Box by Michael Behe

In Six Days by John Ashton

Men of Science, Men of God by Henry Morris

The New Answers Book by Ken Ham et al.

The New Answers Book 2 by Ken Ham et al.

On the Seventh Day by John Ashton

www.answersingenesis.org/go/science

02

THE BIG BANG?

What is a big deal—the biggest deal of all—is how you get something out of nothing. Don't let the cosmologists try to kid you on this one. They have not got a clue either—despite the fact that they are doing a pretty good job of convincing themselves and others that this is really not a problem. "In the beginning," they will say, "there was nothing—no time, space matter or energy. Then there was a quantum fluctuation from which . . ." Whoa! Stop right there. You see what I mean? . . . Then they are away and before you know it, they have pulled a hundred billion galaxies out of their quantum hats.

David Darling, "On Creating Something from Nothing," *New Scientist* 151 (1996): 49.

What You Will Learn

The big bang is the model that a majority of evolutionary scientists believe best explains the origin of the universe. This is why the textbooks present the big bang model as the history of the universe. The big bang suggests that the universe came into existence 13.7 billion years ago. The entire universe was contained in an infinitely small point known as a singularity. This singularity began to expand slowly, then extremely rapidly, and then slowly again, though there is no reason that such changes in rate had to happen. Over time, stars and galaxies began to form through natural processes. These galaxies continue to move away from one another. It is claimed that the biblical time span of 6,000 years cannot explain how light could reach earth from the distant parts of the universe. There are several explanations that potentially solve the light travel-time "problem." The big bang also has its own light travel-time problem, and many other observations limit the age of the universe to much less than 13.7 billion years.

Many people believe that the big bang is compatible with the biblical account of Creation. However, in order to make the big bang fit into the Bible, the biblical explanation is rearranged to conform to the reasoning of secular scientists. The big bang and the Bible are not compatible in the order of events or in the timescale. Attempting to fit scientific ideas into Scripture rather than applying biblical thinking to science leads to compromise and undermines the authority of Scripture.

What Your Textbook Says about the Big Bang

Evolutionary Concept	Prentice Hall	Glencoe	Holt	Articles
Stars form from collapsing nebulae.	707	T745, 793, T794, 812, 822	781–783	2:1
Earth is not at any special place or at the center of the universe.	T6	T832C, T832D, 842	—	2:4
Studying the present universe can help us explain its evolution.	T6, 6	T744, T832D, 832, 854, T854	659, T660, 774, T795	2:1, 2:3, 2:5, 3:6
Globular clusters are 12–14 billion years old.	—	836–837	—	2:1, 2:6
Looking at stars from billions of light years away is like looking back billions of years in time.	—	T832C–T832D, 839, T840, 845–846, 850, 855	717	2:1, 2:5
By studying stars in many different stages of evolution we can understand how stars form and evolve over billions of years.	T6, 707–711	T382, T804A, T804D, T804, T822, 821–822, T823, 824–825, T836–T838, 859, T861, T905, 905	T773A, T773C, T779, 781, T782–T788, 782–788, T797, 797, 805	2:1, 2:3, 2:5, 2:7
A black hole formed early in the formation of our galaxy.	—	836	—	2:7
All elements in the universe formed in the big bang or in the cores of stars.	6, T32C, T711	T745, T804, 804	T773C	2:2

Evolutionary Concept	Prentice Hall	Glencoe	Holt	Articles
Testing shows that the big bang happened over 13 billion years ago, creating the universe, and the universe has been expanding since.	T698C–D, 720	848, T849, 849, 851, T854, 854, 855, 860	660, 675, T773A, 794, 797	2:1, 2:2, 3:6
The steady-state model was proven wrong.	—	848, 849, 855	—	2:1
There was a period of inflation during the early stages of the big bang.	—	850–851, 860	—	2:1, 2:2
The cosmic background radiation supports the big bang model.	T720, 720	T832D, 848, T848, T849, T851, T854, 855	T773D, 795	2:1
The Hubble constant has changed and is used to determine the age of the universe.	—	T850, 850–851	T796	2:1, 2:4
The fate of the universe is either a continued expansion or an eventual collapse.	721	849	—	2:2
The momentum of expansion from the big bang is balanced by the force of gravity.	—	849	—	2:2

Note: Page numbers preceded by "T" indicate items from the teacher notes found in the margins of the Teacher's Edition.

What We Really Know about the Big Bang

Throughout history there have been many views on the origin of the universe. The beliefs range from an eternal universe to a universe that is 6,000 years old—the biblical view. In the last 100 years there have been several naturalistic cosmologic models to explain the existence of the universe. After the description of the theory of relativity by Einstein and calculations showing the vast distance of nebulae (known to be galaxies today) two distinct models were developed. The steady-state model describes an eternal universe in which matter is being continuously created. The big bang model suggests that the universe had a beginning and that it has been expanding since then. The steady-state model held much support in the 1950s and 1960s mainly for philosophical reasons; many people preferred a cosmology in which the universe had no beginning. Traditional cosmological models generally hold that the universe had a beginning, so support for an eternal universe could *prove* that traditional cosmologies were all wrong.

In 1964 the discovery of uniform, low-level radiation called the cosmic microwave background (CMB) was interpreted as strong support for the big bang, and discredited the steady-state model. The big bang model can explain the existence of the CMB while the steady-state model cannot. Since this evidence was published, the big bang model has been the dominant view held by secular scientists. So, what exactly is the big bang and when did it supposedly occur?

Big Bang Model: the cosmological model suggesting the universe began as a single point which expanded to produce the known universe.

It is important to start this discussion with the understanding that the big bang model was developed using naturalistic and uniformitarian principles. We defined naturalism in chapter 1 as a belief denying that an event or object has a supernatural significance. So if the big bang is a naturalistic model then there can be no room for intervention by a Creator. The big bang model is supposed to describe the creation and evolution of the universe by natural laws alone.

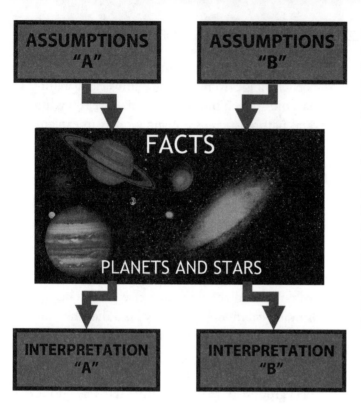

ASSUMPTIONS "A"

ASSUMPTIONS "B"

FACTS

PLANETS AND STARS

INTERPRETATION "A"

INTERPRETATION "B"

Starting with uniformitarian and naturalistic assumptions leads to a different conclusion than does starting with the biblical explanation— God created the universe in a supernatural process. Looking at the same facts through different *lenses* leads to different conclusions.

Uniformitarianism: the doctrine that present-day processes acting at similar rates as observed today account for the change evident in the universe.

We can use radiometric dating as an example to describe how uniformitarianism is related to the big bang and the subsequent development of our solar system. It is assumed by secular scientists that radioactive decay has always occurred at a constant rate. The rate can be used to calculate the age of the rocks if several factors are known. These scientists also assume that as the earth formed there was leftover material that would be the same age as the earth. Using these assumptions, secular scientists believe that meteorites that fall to earth give the best age of the earth since they formed at the same time. Consequently, they have concluded that the solar system must be older than those rocks and the universe even older than that. When you add the assumption of naturalism to the origin of the universe as we know it, you are building a model on multiple unprovable assumptions.

In the big bang model of the origin of the universe, all of the matter, space, and time existed in a "cosmic egg" called a singularity. There is one major problem with this from the uniformitarian view—the known laws of physics fail to describe how the singularity could exist. The idea of cause and effect also fails as there is no known explanation for the cause of the singularity or the cause of the "explosion" that allegedly formed the universe. Scientists who accept that the universe was formed from the big bang must believe that their assumptions are true. Therefore it is a matter of faith to accept that the universe began as an infinitely small point.

Some secular scientists are now suggesting that a quantum fluctuation caused the singularity. If this is the case then what caused the quantum fluctuation? Parallel universes are imagined to explain this idea, but there is no evidence that such universes exist.

The Bible presents a radically different view of the origin of the universe.

Biblical Creation: the supernatural events, occurring over six approximately 24-hour days, described in Genesis 1 and 2, by which God caused the formation of the heaven and earth and everything in them.

Contrary to both naturalistic and uniformitarian assumptions, the Bible clearly teaches a supernatural and rapid origin of the universe. Genesis 1:1 describes the beginning of time, matter, and space with the phrase "In the beginning God created the heavens and the earth." Because this process is supernatural, secular scientists reject that this description of the origin of the universe can be called scientific. Such a claim is unwarranted since there is nothing in science that requires all explanations to be naturalistic.

Biblical Creation Model: a scientific model based on the biblical account of three key events—Creation, the curse of nature brought about by Adam's sin, and the global catastrophe of Noah's Flood.

Secularists claim that the biblical model is based on faith, not on observable, repeatable, testable claims. However, the big bang is also based on faith. The original conditions of the big bang cannot be observed, tested, or repeated by humans and neither can the creation of the universe by God. However, we do have an eyewitness account of the creation of the universe recorded for us by the Creator.

When we look carefully at the beginning assumptions (presuppositions) of those who believe in the big bang and those who believe that God created the universe, we see that it all comes down to where you place your faith. We have the same facts to look at, but the starting assumptions are different. Because we start with different assumptions, we will arrive at different conclusions. This is true in any field of study as we will see throughout this book.

One of the "evidences" that is claimed to prove the universe must be old is the light travel concept. Again, it is not the evidence that must be understood, but the interpretation of the evidence with the assumptions used. From the uniformitarian perspective, light from an object 5 million light-years away should take five million years to reach the earth (a light-year is actually the distance that light travels in one year). The argument against a young earth says that if we can see light from galaxies that are 5 million light-years away, then the universe must be at least 5 million years old. Based on such arguments a majority of scientists claim that the universe is 13.7 billion years old. This is about 2.3 million times older than the 6,000-year age that the Bible presents.

There are several different ways in which this "problem" can be explained. One possibility is that the speed of light has not always been constant. If light had traveled much faster in the past then light from distant galaxies would have arrived at the earth much faster and the age of the universe would be much younger than 13.7 billion years old. However, there are still questions about whether this is a valid option and researchers are currently working on this idea. The problem comes from the relationship between the speed of light and other universal constants. If the speed of light were to be dramatically different, then this would affect the other constants as well.

Another explanation—called time dilation—is related to gravity. Time flows more slowly when something is near a massive object. Time is also affected by velocity. If we could accelerate a clock to near the speed of light, the clock would slow down as time itself is slowed. Time actually flows at different rates in different parts of the universe depending on the amount of gravity present. In fact, this effect can actually be measured on earth. Since a mountain top is farther from the mass of the earth than sea level is, there is less gravitational potential there. Thus, a clock at the top of the mountain will actually run faster than a clock at sea level. The difference on earth is extremely small, but the difference between other areas of the universe can be quite large.

If the earth is near the center of a finite, expanding universe, then the clocks on earth would have been running slowly compared to clocks in deep space. This allows light to travel from distant galaxies while only a few thousand years pass on earth. Many scientists believe that the universe is infinitely large, and they reject the above explanations based on this assumption. There is no reason the universe must be infinite—it is simply a belief. Changing the assumptions changes the conclusions even though the data remain the same.

The third explanation centers on synchronization. On earth there are different ways to synchronize clocks—to set them to read the same time at the same time. One way (called "universal time") is to synchronize them by radio or some other signal so that all clocks on earth read the same time as in Greenwich. Another method called "local time" sets clocks to noon when the sun reaches its highest point in the sky. An airplane leaving Georgia at 1:00 local time could (in principle) arrive in California at 1:00 local time even though the trip would take three hours as measured in universal time. Likewise, time in space can be measured by "cosmic universal time" or "cosmic local time." Light traveling toward earth will always reach its destination at the same cosmic local time that it left—just like the plane traveling from Georgia to California. No matter how far away a galaxy is, its light can reach earth on the same day it leaves, as measured by cosmic local time.

Although there is presently no clear answer as to which of these models, or combination of their parts, provides the most satisfactory explanation, Bible–believing Christians can still rest assured that God has revealed truth to us in the Bible. Starting with the Bible as a foundation for thinking about the world leads to a different interpretation of the data than does starting with the assumptions of naturalism and uniformitarianism.

Most people who believe in the big bang do not realize that it has its own light travel-time problem. This difficulty is known as the *horizon problem*. In the big bang model the universe starts as a singularity and then expands from there. As mentioned earlier, the CMB shows that the universe has a very uniform temperature of about 2.7 K (-455°F). Some parts of the expanding universe were certainly hotter than others. So, imagine two points A and B in the universe separated by 20 billion light years. If A and B have the same temperature today then they must have exchanged energy to reach a uniform temperature.

The fastest way that these two distant points in space can exchange energy is by exchanging electromagnetic radiation. Electromagnetic radiation comes in the form of X-rays, microwaves, radio waves, and light. If A was slightly hotter than B, as the big bang model predicts, then they would have had to exchange energy until the temperature reached a state of equilibrium. There is not enough time in the alleged 13.7 billion years for the equilibrium temperature to be reached if the universe has been expanding in a uniform way.

To resolve the *horizon problem*, big bang supporters have suggested that there was a period of inflation, or a burst of expansion, in the first fractions of a second after the universe began to expand. The problem is that there is no evidence or reason to suggest there was an inflationary period other than to avoid the *horizon problem*. The Glencoe textbook refers to this as a "correction . . . needed to allow for the fact that the expansion was more rapid at the

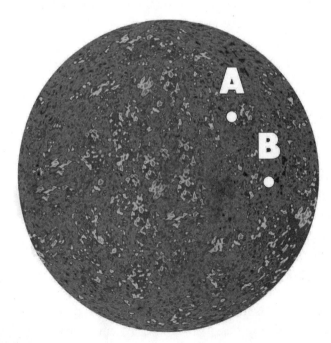

The claim that the biblical creation model has a light time-travel problem is a self refuting argument against the big bang model. The big bang model has a similar difficulty known as the *horizon problem*.

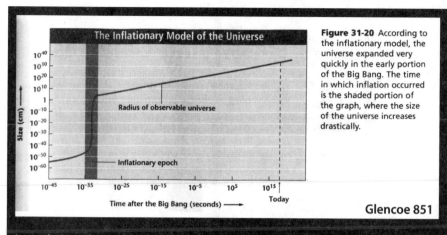

Figure 31-20 According to the inflationary model, the universe expanded very quickly in the early portion of the Big Bang. The time in which inflation occurred is the shaded portion of the graph, where the size of the universe increases drastically.

Glencoe 851

According to this graph, the inflationary period occurred before the universe was 1 cm in diameter (about the width of your finger) and in an incomprehensibly small amount of time. This allows for the Cosmic Microwave Background to become uniform, but there is no known mechanism to explain how the inflation began and then ended. Despite this shortcoming, supporters of the big bang must accept the "fact" of inflation.

beginning . . ." on page 851. The *inflation solution* to the *horizon problem* is nothing more than a story to support a belief about the past. To add to the problem, there is no well-established reason for the inflationary period to have occurred and no explanation of how it slowed itself down in a smooth fashion. Despite these observational shortcomings, most big bang supporters adhere to the *fact* of the inflationary phase.

The biblical creation model of the universe is rejected as unscientific by a majority of scientists on the grounds that it is supernatural or that it is just a story. As described above, the big bang seems to fit this description as well. There is no explanation for the existence of this singularity, and "corrections" must be made to account for what we actually observe. Both of the models are based on faith in the starting conditions. One key difference is that Christians have an eyewitness account of the beginning of the universe in the Bible. There is no similar record for big bang supporters.

Another major difference in the biblical creation and big bang models is the ultimate end of the universe. In the big bang model, there are two possible outcomes. In an open or flat universe the matter and space continue to expand until the temperature becomes uniform. This is often called the heat death as everything

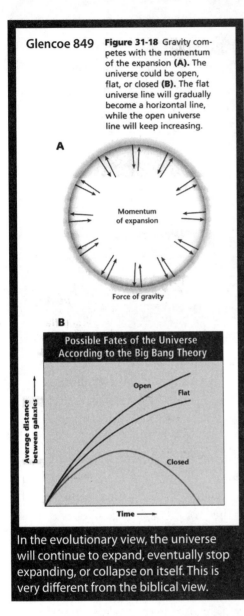

Glencoe 849

Figure 31-18 Gravity competes with the momentum of the expansion (**A**). The universe could be open, flat, or closed (**B**). The flat universe line will gradually become a horizontal line, while the open universe line will keep increasing.

A

Momentum of expansion

Force of gravity

B

Possible Fates of the Universe According to the Big Bang Theory

Average distance between galaxies →

Open

Flat

Closed

Time →

In the evolutionary view, the universe will continue to expand, eventually stop expanding, or collapse on itself. This is very different from the biblical view.

in the universe reaches absolute zero temperature. In a closed universe the matter and space will eventually collapse on themselves in a *big crunch*. All of these outcomes are contrary to the description given in the Bible. God declares that He will make a new heaven and earth and that the original earth will be consumed by fire—the exact opposite of heat death.

There are many other observations that are not explained by the big bang model and a universe that is 13.7 billion years old. A few of those will be discussed here, and a more comprehensive list can be found in the reference articles at the end of this chapter. One major problem is how the most distant visible galaxies appear. Big bang supporters claim that to look at a galaxy that is 12 billion light-years away is to look at the universe as it existed 12 billion years ago. In fact, images from the Hubble Deep Field show fully-formed galaxies in the early universe—an unexpected observation in the big bang model.

Many of the galaxies in the universe, including our own Milky Way, have a spiral shape with long arms extending from a central disc. If these galaxies were truly billions of years old, their arms would have been twisted into uniformity because the center spins faster than the outer edges. Their shape is not a problem if the galaxies are only 6,000 years old.

There are too few supernova remnants to account for many billions of years. Star formation has never been observed, and there are far too many "short-lived" stars for the universe to be billions of years old. Other problems related to the formation of our solar system will be discussed in the next chapter.

As we discuss this topic, it is important to note that many Christians want to believe that God used the big bang to create the universe. In effect, these people are trying to blend the ideas of naturalism with Scripture. There are many problems with this position, which is commonly referred to as old-earth creationism. There are many different variations on this idea, and many of them are related to the day-age interpretation of Genesis 1 and 2. The general argument is that the days described in the Creation account of Genesis are actually long periods of different ages. This view is a recent invention of man and has come about only after naturalistic science *proved* that the earth and universe must be billions of years old. You can find more information on these different compromise positions by visiting www.answersingenesis.org/go/compromise.

There are many problems to resolve for those Christians who try to blend man's fallible ideas about the history of the universe with the Creator's clear explanation of the events. Many may not realize how different the two positions really are. There was a time in my life where I thought that God used the big bang to create the universe. I was never taught this directly; it just seemed to make sense from what little I knew about the Bible. As I studied the Bible it became obvious that the two positions cannot be reconciled without twisting Scripture to accommodate the ideas of evolutionary science. The Bible is to be the authority in every aspect of our lives as Scripture commands in 2 Corinthians 10:4–5:

> For the weapons of our warfare are not carnal but
> mighty in God for pulling down strongholds, casting
> down arguments and every high thing that exalts itself
> against the knowledge of God, bringing every thought
> into captivity to the obedience of Christ.

Every thought is to be brought "into captivity to the obedience of Christ" who is the Word of God. Adding science to Scripture and changing the clear meaning of Scripture makes man and his pseudo-scientific thinking the authority over the Bible. The following table points out some of the direct contradictions between the Bible and the big bang.

Table 2-1: Incompatibility of the Bible and the Big Bang

Bible	Big Bang
Earth before the sun	Sun before the earth
Light on earth before the sun	Sun before light on earth
Earth before the stars	Stars before the earth
6,000-year-old universe	13.7-billion-year-old universe
Not subject to change	Subject to change and may be totally rejected for a different model
Inspired by a perfect God	Invented by fallible men

This is a condensed list, and more details will be discussed in the next chapter. In order to harmonize the secular order of events with the biblical order, we must put Day Four before Day One to get light on the earth. If we do this, we compromise the authority of Scripture and tell God that He really should have explained things in a different order than He used in Genesis. This low view of Scripture ultimately leads to compromise in other areas. If God got it wrong in Genesis, where else did He get it wrong? We cannot allow naturalistic science—based in human reasoning—to become the authority over Scripture!

The Bible and the big bang present completely different accounts of the origin of the universe. Ultimately, both positions must be based on faith in the starting assumptions. Understanding the assumptions that inform your decisions is the key to understanding the issues involved.

Reference Article Summaries

2:1 Does distant starlight prove the universe is old? Lisle, www. answersingenesis.org/articles/nab/does-starlight-prove

Critics of biblical creation often use the argument that light from distant stars requires billions of years to reach earth and, therefore, the earth must be much older than 6,000 years. To get around this problem, some creationists have suggested that the distances measured must be wrong, but these distances are based on solid, observational science. Another common claim is that the light we see today was created on its way to earth. Many aspects of the created universe must have appeared mature at the time of their creation (Adam was not an infant), but light from distant objects is different. If the light from a supernova that recently exploded was created in transit, then that star never really existed—we saw an image of a nonexistent event. It seems uncharacteristic of God to use an illusion to portray the natural world.

Anytime we try to estimate the age of things, we must make assumptions. If any of the assumptions are questionable, then the argument is not sound. The first assumption is that the speed of light has always been constant. Changing the speed of light has effects on other aspects of physics including the relationship between mass and energy in a system ($E=mc^2$). Some creation scientists believe this is a valid model to explain distant starlight while others believe we should look for another explanation.

Another assumption is that time is rigid. However, time is dependent on the velocity and the strength of gravity where the time is being measured. This may seem strange, but it has been demonstrated by experimentation and is a sound scientific idea. Since time can flow at different rates from different points of view, events could occur at different positions in the universe. Only a short amount of time has passed on earth while there has been more time passing at the far reaches of the universe. There is a question as to the amount of difference that creationist models using this idea can produce, and more research needs to be done.

Another assumption is that time is measured by the "cosmic universal time" convention. However, we commonly use time zone conventions on earth, and these same ideas can be applied to the universe. The language in the Bible may be explaining the light visible in the universe using cosmic local time rather than cosmic universal time. This is an intriguing way to look at the alleged problem.

The final assumption is that the universe may only be explained by naturalism. This assumption automatically cuts any supernatural explanation, especially the God of the Bible, out of the picture. Some secularists argue that a supernatural act cannot be true on the basis that it cannot be explained by natural processes observed today. This is a circular argument and rejects, as a starting assumption, the existence of a God who can act outside of the natural laws He created.

In spite of these assumptions, the naturalistic explanation has its own light travel-time problem that is rarely discussed. The universe is so large that there has not been enough time for light to travel from one side to the other. In the secular view, the uniform temperature of the cosmic microwave background must be explained by natural processes alone. For the temperature to become uniform, different areas must exchange energy. The fastest way to do this is to exchange electromagnetic radiation (light) since nothing can travel faster than light. Since the points are farther apart than the light could travel (see diagram on page 48) there is no way, using the naturalistic assumptions, that the temperature could be as uniform as it is.

To explain this problem away, secular scientists have suggested there was an inflationary period in the very early stages of the big bang. There is no evidence to support this idea other than *it must be so* if the big bang is an accurate model of the formation of the universe. The inflationary models actually create more problems to solve. Since the big bang has its own light travel-time problem, it is inconsistent to use a light travel-time problem to discredit the biblical explanation.

There are many problems with the big bang and there are many evidences that suggest the universe cannot be billions of years old. Since all of these explanations of the age of the universe rely on assumptions, there must be an objective standard to know which is true. Because the Bible contains the eyewitness record of the Creator, it should be our standard for determining truth.

2:2 Does the big bang fit with the Bible? Lisle, www.answersingenesis.org/articles/wow/does-the-big-bang-fit

The big bang is a story about how the universe came into existence. It proposes that the universe began billions of years ago as a singularity that contained all of the space and energy of the universe. The singularity expanded rapidly, and the energy cooled and turned into hydrogen and helium gas. These elements formed the first stars and then eventually galaxies and planets—including earth. Many people, including Christians, accept the big bang as fact even though it is only a story. Many Christians distort the plain reading of Scripture to accommodate the atheistic underpinnings of the big bang.

Since the big bang model was developed to explain the origin of the universe without the Bible, it is not wise to attempt to blend the two together. The Bible clearly teaches that the universe was created in six days and in an order that is contrary to the order of the big bang. For example, the big bang teaches that the stars were formed before the earth, and the Bible teaches that the earth was formed three days before the stars.

The big bang also teaches that the universe will likely end in a frozen state as it runs out of energy. The Bible teaches that the world will be judged, and a new heaven and earth will be created—the two ideas are not compatible.

Apart from the biblical problems, there are scientific problems with the big bang. The big bang predicts that there should be many monopoles present from the high temperatures of the big bang, but these monopoles have never been found. The random nature of the big bang makes

it unlikely that the universe would be balanced between the momentum of expansion and the force of gravity. If this balance were not present, the universe would rapidly fly apart or collapse on itself. A period of rapid expansion, called the inflation period, has been suggested to address these and other problems. There is, however, no evidence to support the inflation period, and how it would start and stop is not understood.

Another missing element of the universe is the antimatter predicted by the big bang model. There should be equal amounts of matter and antimatter present, but we see only trace amounts of antimatter. If the universe were created by God for life, it would contain only matter.

The absence of Population III stars (stars containing only hydrogen, helium, and lithium), which should be left over from the earliest stages of the big bang universe, is another strike against the model. All stars found so far contain heavier elements that were supposedly created in the cores of stars that exploded in the past. The presence of these elements in all known stars in our galaxy, over 100 billion, is hard to explain in light of the big bang.

Numerous secular scientists are abandoning the modern big bang theory because of its many problems. What will

Christians who accept the big bang as support for the Bible do when another model is adopted by secular scientists? Secular models constantly change, but God's word can be trusted; there is no need to compromise Scripture to understand the universe. Ultimately, the best reason to reject the big bang is that the Creator has taught that He created everything in a way that is contrary to the big bang.

2:3 New Stars, New Planets? DeYoung, www.icr.org/article/403/

Evolutionists must assume that new stars are constantly forming to replace those that are dying out. Nebulae have been called "star nurseries" and the origin of new stars. The formation of a new star has never been observed, as it is supposed to take hundreds of thousands of years for a dust cloud to collapse and form a new star.

From a creationist perspective, the universe we observe today is virtually the same as it would have appeared to Adam and Eve. All of the stars that we see today are *young* stars.

Astronomers have looked for new stars in the formative stages and have found only a few areas of compressing gas. This is far short of what would be needed to explain the existence of billions upon billions of stars. The fact that there is no mechanism to explain the formation of stars from nebula without the existence of other stars is a major problem for secular theories of star formation.

Evolutionists reason that if the earth formed from a disk of dust and gas as our sun was forming, then there must be other planets like earth in the universe. If there are other planets like earth, then life must have evolved elsewhere in the universe. There have been several planets detected by indirect methods, but none are similar to earth. To add to the problems, the planets do not seem to fit the expectations of the theories of planet formation. The planets are too large and near their suns to have evolved, let alone have life evolving on them. The claims of the presence of water on such planets, a hallmark of the evolution of life in the minds of the evolutionists, are overstated and based on many assumptions.

2:4 Our galaxy is the centre of the universe, "quantized" red shifts show, Humphreys, www.answersingenesis.org/tj/v16/i2/galaxy.asp

Over the last few decades, new evidence has surfaced that restores man to a central place in God's universe. Astronomers have confirmed that numerical values of galaxy redshifts are "quantized," tending to fall into distinct groups. According to Hubble's law, redshifts are proportional to the distances of the galaxies from us. Then it would be the distances themselves that fall into groups. That would mean the galaxies tend to be grouped into (conceptual) spherical shells concentric around our home galaxy, the Milky Way. The shells turn out to be on the order of a million light years apart. The groups of redshifts would be distinct from each other only if our viewing location is less than a million light years from the center. The odds for the earth having such a unique position in the cosmos by accident are less than one in a trillion. Since big bang theorists presuppose the cosmos has naturalistic origins and cannot have a unique center, they have sought other explanations, without notable success so far. Thus, redshift quantization is evidence (1) against the big bang theory, and (2) for a galactocentric cosmology.

2:5 Young galaxies too old for the big bang, Rigg, www.answersingenesis.org/creation/v26/i3/galaxies.asp

Astronomers have found a string of galaxies at the very edge of the universe, 10.8 billion light years away. Using uniformitarian assumptions, these galaxies formed a few billion years after the big bang. According to big bang models, these galaxies should be small and unorganized. The maturity of these galaxies is evidence that the big bang models are not accurate. By starting with naturalistic assumptions, rather than God's Word, the data is misinterpreted.

2:6 The globular cluster bomb, Coppedge, www.icr.org/article/3150/

The presence of globular clusters is a problem for big bang models that suggest the clusters formed shortly after the big bang. The presence of stars of mixed "age" has discredited earlier ideas about the formation of these clusters. The models of star formation in globular clusters must be changed but it is safe to assume the big bang model will not be questioned in light of the new evidence.

2:7 Black holes: the evidence of things not seen, Lisle, www.answersingenesis.org/articles/am/v3/n1/black-holes-evidence

In 1783, British scientist John Michell postulated the idea of a "dark star"—a star with gravity so strong that even light cannot escape. Is this possible? Einstein changed the ideas surrounding gravity by supposing that gravity is not a force, but the *bending* of space and time. In essence, gravity imparts a sort of velocity to empty space, and matter moves along with it. Imagine sailboats on a lake and a river. Gravity was once thought to be like the wind pushing the boat through the water—which is space in the analogy. In reality, gravity moves space itself and brings the matter along with it, much as the current in a river would move the boat.

Photons (particles of light) are like motorboats moving at a constant speed, but their motion is affected by the movement of the water. Light, in a similar manner, can be bent as it travels through moving space. A black hole has such a strong gravitational field that it pulls space so fast even light cannot escape. This would be like a lake with a drain in the middle pulling the water so quickly that the motorboats close to the drain could not escape. The boundary where the velocity of light moving away is equal to the speed that space is being pulled into the black hole is called the event horizon.

The black hole is not a star, as Michell proposed, but the gravity is so strong that the mass is all contained in a point called a singularity. You could never see any events within the event horizon. This is so because no light could escape the gravitational field which pulls the space toward the singularity at a speed faster than light. The gravitational field can cause objects to orbit the black hole, but the field is so strong that even light can orbit a black hole.

If light cannot escape from black holes, then how could we ever find one? Binary star systems consist of two stars orbiting one another. Some of these systems should contain black holes, and one of the stars would be invisible. Cygnus X-1 is a binary system that contains a blue supergiant orbiting an invisible body with enough mass to be a black hole. X-rays can also be used to detect black holes, and many observations confirm their existence. Black holes provide an observable confirmation of Einstein's theory of relativity—the basis for cosmologies that explain how light can reach earth from distant galaxies in thousands of years or less. Black holes, and other scientific discoveries, give us a small glimpse into the thoughts of an infinite God (Psalm 19:1).

Questions to Consider

1. If new stars form as the result of exploding stars compressing nebulae, then how did the first stars form if there were no stars to compress the gases?

2. If it is true that when we look at objects nearly 11 billion light years away we are seeing them as they appeared 11 billion years ago, why are the galaxies that we see at great distances fully formed (mature) when the big bang model predicts they should be less organized at that early stage?

3. The textbook avoids discussing things like dark matter and dark energy that are not observed but assumed to exist. How is the big bang a scientific theory if it is based on the existence of evidence that has not been observed?

4. If the universe was created by the energy from the big bang then there would have been an equal amount of matter and antimatter created as the universe cooled. Have scientists been able to find any antimatter? How much has been found?

5. What caused the inflationary period in the big bang?

6. What evidence is there to support the inflationary period of the big bang?

7. Is the big bang the only way to explain the expansion of the universe?

8. Why is the big bang, which cannot be observed, considered scientific while supernatural creation is rejected as unscientific?

9. How did the natural laws of the universe come from the random big bang?

Tools for Digging Deeper

The New Answers Book by Ken Ham et al.

The New Answers Book 2 by Ken Ham et al.

Our Created Moon by Don DeYoung

Starlight and Time by Russell Humphreys

Taking Back Astronomy by Jason Lisle

Universe by Design by Danny Faulkner

www.answersingenesis.org/go/astronomy

ORIGIN OF THE SOLAR SYSTEM

Many scientific papers are written each year about the Oort Cloud, its properties, its origin, its evolution. Yet there is not yet a shred of direct observational evidence for its existence.

Carl Sagan and Ann Druyan, *Comets* (New York, New York: Random House, 1985), p. 201.

What You Will Learn

The naturalistic story of the solar system goes back 4.5 billion years. In this view the solar system began as a cloud of dust and gas that collapsed on itself. A star began to form as the cloud was compressed by some unknown force. As the star spun and collected more mass, a disk of dust began to form the planets. Over millions of years the young solar system was formed. Much debris was left over from the process and is present today as asteroids and large belts and clouds of material. There was no intervention by a Creator, as the physical laws of the universe are adequate to explain everything—or so say the evolutionists.

The Bible reveals a much different story, and there are many problems with the models and hypotheses that are used to support the story described above. Artists' depictions of the events make them look real, but they are just a story to explain why God is not necessary. Among the problems are a slowly spinning sun, the moon's closeness to the earth, and a "chicken-and-egg" problem with star formation. The differences between what the Bible teaches and what the evolutionary perspective teaches are many and significant. It is impossible to reconcile the two explanations without twisting Scripture or rewriting the history revealed in Genesis.

What Your Textbook Says about the Origin of the Solar System

Evolutionary Concept	Prentice Hall	Glencoe	Holt	Articles
The solar system formed from a collapsing, spinning nebula.	2, 3–5, T642C, T646, 647, 706	744, 793–794, T794, T797, 797, 801, 836–838, 855, 858–859	216, T317C, T683C, 685–687, T686–T687, 791	3:1, 3:3, 3:4, 3:5, 3:13, 5:1
Planets form from colliding particles at different distances from the sun.	648	648, 793, T794, T800	35, T687, T688, 701–702, T703, 709	3:1, 3:2, 3:3, 3:5, 3:13
Earth formed from a molten ball, and the layers formed as earth cooled.	5, T64C, 367	T98C, 101, T270C, 576–579, 580, T694	6, 148, T687–T688, 688, 709	3:6
The earth's atmosphere, including oxygen, and oceans formed gradually as earth cooled.	5, 367, 477, 495	9, T270C, 387–388, T576C, 584, 585–587, 648–649, 664, 679, 740	T209C, T545C, T688–T689, 689–690, 698	3:6, 3:7, 3:8, 3:9, 3:16
The moon formed from a collision over 4 billion years ago and has changed little in 3 billion years.	T612C, 631, 633–634	648, T755, 755, T756, 756–757, T764, 764, 771, 858	153, T717C, T719, 719–724, T723, 726, 745	3:2, 3:10, 3:11
Earth's tilt and precession cycle over tens of thousands of years.	601, T612, 622	372–373	T632, 643	3:2, 4:3, 5:2, 5:3
Asteroids are leftover debris from the formation of the solar system.	664	504, T774A, T774D, 795–796, T797, 801, 858–859	718, 723, 739, 740, 744	3:1, 3:13
Many moons in our solar system may have been captured.	657, 658	784, 792	T734, 737	3:1, 3:11

Evolutionary Concept	Prentice Hall	Glencoe	Holt	Articles
Cratering can be used to determine the age of planets and moons.	634, 652	784	695, 733, 735	3:4, 3:12
The planets have changed size and rotational direction since their formation.	—	781–782, 789	697, 699, T705	3:4, 3:5, 3:14
Planetary ring systems may be very young features.	—	—	T717D	3:15
The presence of water in the solar system may support life.	—	T774C, T784, 784–785, T787	665, T699, 700	3:7, 3:17
Comets originate in the Kuiper belt and the Oort cloud and orbit over hundreds or thousands of years.	661– 663	796–797	T683D, 739, T741–T743, 742–743, T745, 745, T773, 773	3:2, 3:13, 5:1
The fact that the sun and moon appear the same size is a coincidence, not a result of creation.	T672C	T859	—	2:2
The sun formed about 5 billion years ago and will last another 5 billion years.	6, 690, T710, 716	657, T682D, T804A, 810–811, 821–823, T825, 835	756, 791	3:16

Note: Page numbers preceded by "T" indicate items from the teacher notes found in the margins of the Teacher's Edition.

What We Really Know about the Origin of the Solar System

According to the secular scenario, energy was gradually converted into matter as the universe continued to expand after the big bang. That matter accumulated and the first atoms began to form. The first stages of the naturalistic universe contained only energy. As the expanding universe slowed and cooled, hydrogen, helium, and small amounts of lithium were formed from the energy. The gases gathered into nebulae which then gave birth to stars and planets. As the earliest stars produced their energy through nuclear fusion, heavier elements were assembled and were eventually scattered into the universe as the stars exploded. These heavier elements accumulated in the universe over billions of years, and star systems with planets began to form.

Star formation and stellar evolution have never been observed because they are supposed to occur over many millions of years. Evolutionists suggest that the stars form as gases (hydrogen and helium in the early universe) collapse due to gravity. As the nebula collapses, the gases heat up and the nebula spins itself into a flattened disk. One major problem with this scenario is that as the gases are heated, the pressure increases. This pressure would tend to cause the nebula to expand and counteract the gravitational collapse.

To counter this problem, it is suggested that some type of "shock" overcomes the gas pressure at just the right time. This shock may come from the explosion of a nearby supernova or some other source. The problem has now become a circular argument. In order for the first stars to form, there would have had to have been other stars reaching the supernova stage to cause the first stars to form. So the argument may work for later generations of stars but it cannot explain how the first generation formed. If the first generation couldn't form, then they could not have produced the materials and force for later generations to form.

Setting the previous problem aside, evolutionists would then suggest that a protostar would form and continue to gain mass as it attracted nearby gas and particles. If the pressure in the core of the star increases the temperature to 10 million Kelvin degrees, nuclear fusion can begin and the star becomes stable. The stability comes

Glencoe 822

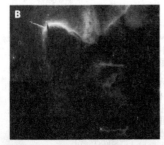

A — Infalling material

Protostar

Rotating disk

Figure 30-19 A protostar, formed from a disk of gas and dust **(A)**, will become a star when fusion begins. The Triffid Nebula **(B)** is illuminated by new stars, as shown by the *Hubble Space Telescope*.

B

STELLAR EVOLUTION AND LIFE CYCLES

A star changes as it ages because its internal composition changes as nuclear fusion reactions in the star's core convert one element into another. As a star's core composition changes, its density increases, its temperature rises, and its luminosity increases. Eventually, the nuclear fuel runs out. Then the star's internal structure and mechanism for producing pressure must change to counteract gravity.

The formation of a protostar over millions of years from a spinning nebula has been proposed to explain the birth of new stars. There are many problems with this scenario and no explanation of how the first stars could have formed according to the known laws of physics. The Bible explains that God made the stars on Day Four.

when the inward gravitational force balances the outward gas pressure. Depending on the size and composition of the star, it follows a multi-billion year process until it consumes all of its nuclear fuel. At the end of its life it will either contract and become a white dwarf or explode in a spectacular supernova and leave behind a black hole or a neutron star. Our own sun is expected to complete this cycle in the next 5 billion years. This obviously assumes a uniformitarian progression of time and matter into the unreachable future.

Exactly how this process proceeded in our solar system is a matter of inferring events in the past from what we see in the present. As discussed earlier, there are certain assumptions that must be made when creating historical theories. The ideas presented in the textbooks are based on uniformitarian assumptions and have many problems that are not discussed, despite the presence of phrases like "we know" and "scientists have shown."

One uniformitarian belief presented in the textbooks is the formation of elements that make up the universe. The textbooks suggest that all of the matter in the universe is a result of the big bang. Atoms larger than hydrogen (with the exception of some helium and trace amounts of lithium which also formed from the energy of the big bang) are believed to be formed in the core of stars as a result of nuclear fusion. This process can only explain the presence of elements up to the mass of iron. It is suggested that the elements heavier than iron formed as a result of supernovae exploding. These elements were scattered into the universe and were eventually gathered by forming stars and planets.

The heavier elements found on the earth were produced in a supernova and were collected as the solar system formed. This stands in direct opposition to the creation of the earth described in Genesis. The Bible presents the view that God created the entire universe, including each individual atom, out of nothing in six days, not from the constant process of stellar evolution over billions of years. The Bible teaches that the earth was formed on Day One and the stars on Day Four through the spoken words of God—the two ideas are quite opposite.

The formation of our solar system is thought to be typical of other star systems in the universe. Around 5 billion years ago, an interstellar cloud of dust and gases began to collapse on itself as the force of gravity pulled the particles together. This scenario presents a problem. The force of gravity is pulling the particles together but other forces, like the pressure exerted by the gases in a balloon, are pushing the particles apart. Gravity is a relatively weak force, and this model has great difficulty in explaining how the stars and planets actually formed.

The model used by evolutionists to describe the formation of star systems is called the nebular hypothesis.

Nebular Hypothesis: belief that the solar system formed form a spinning, collapsing nebula; the sun formed at the center with the planets forming at various distances.

The idea was first put forth in the 1700s and has undergone minor revisions. Our solar system allegedly began as a nebula that began to spin and collapse due to gravity. As the nebula spun faster and faster, the protostar began to form (as described above) and a disk of dust and gases surrounded the protostar. The

The nebular hypothesis is simply a story to describe what may have happened in the "prehistoric" solar system. There are no observations to support the claims that natural processes over millions of years could form a solar system. The Bible gives a clear description of the formation of the earth by the spoken word of God.

Figure 3 Formation of the Universe A According to the nebular theory, the solar system formed from a rotating cloud of dust and gas. **B** The sun formed at the center of the rotating disk. **C** Planetismals collided, eventually gaining enough mass to be planets.

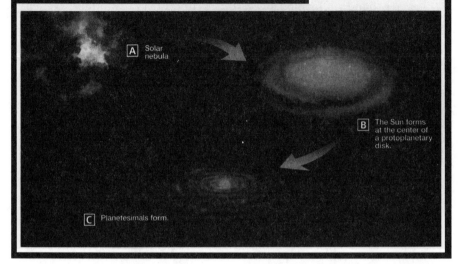

A Solar nebula

B The Sun forms at the center of a protoplanetary disk.

C Planetesimals form.

spinning nebular disk was warmer at the center than at the edges. Planetesimals began to slowly form as the dust particles stuck to one another.

The planetesimals that formed closer to the center of the disk contained the rocky elements like iron and silica that have high melting points. The lighter elements and compounds were blown away from the center and began to accumulate in the outer planetesimals. The outer planets are made of gases and ices as well as some rocky components. Over time, the planetesimals supposedly collided with one another or stuck together through gravitational attraction. As the collisions continued, the planets were born. Over time, most of the dust was gathered by the planets' gravity, and the solar system became stable as the orbits of the major planets were established. Small dust particles and many asteroids still orbit the sun and are believed to be the leftover debris from the formation of the solar system.

One of the biggest problems with this explanation of the solar system is that the particles of dust must stick together, known as

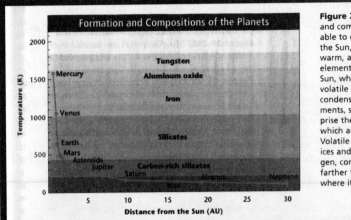

Figure 29-28 Elements and compounds that were able to condense close to the Sun, where it was warm, are called refractory elements, and far from the Sun, where it was cool, volatile elements could condense. Refractory elements, such as iron, comprise the terrestrial planets, which are close to the Sun. Volatile elements, such as ices and gases like hydrogen, comprise the planets farther from the Sun, where it is cool.

Glencoe 794

The formation of a solar system has never been observed. These photos from the Hubble Space Telescope show what evolutionists believe to be the formation of a new star or solar system within nebulae. However, these are areas of hot gases, so they are more likely dispersing than collapsing. These could also be old, cold stars collecting gas and dust from the surrounding cloud. More data needs to be gathered for the conclusions to be accepted.

accretion, to form the planetesimals. The stardust particles that are supposed to have formed the solar system would have just bounced off one another. The particles in the rings of Saturn offer a model for what would have happened in the spinning disk of the young solar system. If the particles were moving faster, they would still bounce off of one another or explode as they collided with great force. Again, the nebular hypothesis is a story of what must have happened even though there is no evidence in support of the claims.

Another significant problem with the formation of the solar system is caused by the spin of the forming system. As more of the mass is pulled toward the sun, the mass must spin faster according to the Law of Conservation of Angular Momentum. This law is easily demonstrated. Sit on an office chair with your arms and legs extended and have someone spin you. Pull your arms and legs into the center and you will spin faster. This is similar to what should have happened to the sun in the nebular hypothesis.

If the nebular hypothesis were accurate, the sun would be spinning much faster than it is. The sun has only 2% of the angular momentum and 99% of the mass of the solar system. To explain away this obvious problem, evolutionists propose a mechanism of magnetic field braking. The precise details of magnetic braking are still debated, but it must have happened for the nebular hypothesis to be accepted.

Other remnants of the naturalistic formation of the solar system are the Kuiper belt objects and comets. The Kuiper belt lies outside of the orbit of Neptune and is the alleged source of short-period comets. Comets that orbit the sun in more than 200 years are believed to come from the Oort cloud. The Oort cloud is a hypothetical sphere of icy masses that no one has ever seen. Despite this fact the Holt text says on page 742:

> The Oort cloud surrounds the solar system and may reach as far as halfway to the nearest star. Scientists think that the matter in the Oort cloud was left over from the formation of the solar system. Studying this distant matter helps scientists understand the early history of the universe. Bodies within the Oort cloud circle the sun so slowly that they take a few million years to complete one orbit.

Despite never seeing the Oort cloud, we are told by the text that it surrounds the solar system, it has a huge size, was left over from the formation of the solar system, and its bodies take millions of years to orbit. All of these are "facts" that have been made up to fit the facts that are actually observed. So why is it necessary for evolutionists to invent the Oort cloud?

As comets orbit the sun the solar wind blasts off parts of the comet. Such debris is visible as the tails of the comet. Each time a comet orbits the sun it loses about 1% of its mass. Halley's Comet orbits the earth every 76 years, so it is constantly losing mass. If Halley's Comet is left over from the beginning of the solar system 4.5 billion years ago, all of its mass would have been lost billions of years ago. This is not a problem for a universe that is 6,000 years old, as the Bible describes. In order to explain the presence of comets in an old universe, evolutionists suggest that comets are continuously knocked out of the Kuiper belt or the Oort cloud. The logic is as follows:

> If comets are remnants of the formation of the solar system, they lose their mass in a few hundred orbits, and the solar system is 4.5 billion years old, then new

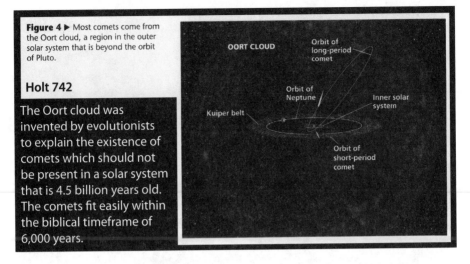

Figure 4 ▶ Most comets come from the Oort cloud, a region in the outer solar system that is beyond the orbit of Pluto.

OORT CLOUD

Orbit of long-period comet

Orbit of Neptune

Inner solar system

Kuiper belt

Orbit of short-period comet

Holt 742

The Oort cloud was invented by evolutionists to explain the existence of comets which should not be present in a solar system that is 4.5 billion years old. The comets fit easily within the biblical timeframe of 6,000 years.

comets must be added to the solar system or we would not see comets today.

The problem is that this is an explanation based on zero observations and the assumption that the solar system is 4.5 billion years old. This is not a valid scientific model although it is accepted by most scientists as "the way it must be." Comets confirm a young universe, not an imaginary cloud in the sky.

The age and formation of the earth need to be addressed in a special way because earth is the planet that we live on. In the nebular hypothesis the earth formed as a molten mass in the early solar system. The heat was generated by many collisions with other bodies orbiting the forming sun. As the earth cooled, the materials separated into layers based on their density—the less dense materials near the surface and the more dense materials in the core. Once again, this is in direct opposition to what the Bible teaches. Genesis 1:2–6 makes it clear that the earth was created as a ball covered with water. In the naturalistic scenario, the oceans come much later, only after the earth has cooled over millions of years.

The textbooks explain that as the earth continued to cool, the atmosphere was formed and volcanoes released gas into the young atmosphere. The young atmosphere was supposedly composed of nitrogen, carbon dioxide, sulfur oxides, methane, and ammonia. The obvious missing ingredient is oxygen. Many evolutionists believe that oxygen was not a part of the atmosphere until hundreds of millions of years later when bacteria evolved the ability to

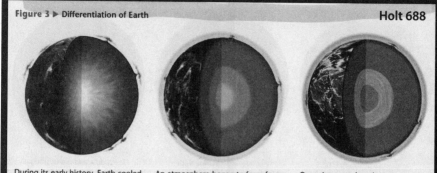

Figure 3 ▶ Differentiation of Earth **Holt 688**

During its early history, Earth cooled to form three distinct layers.

An atmosphere began to form from the water vapor and carbon dioxide released by volcanic eruptions.

Organisms produced oxygen from photosynthesis to create an oxygenated atmosphere.

Evolutionists create a story about the earth cooling from a molten mass about 4.5 billion years ago. The pictures and stories are simply the products of imaginations that try to explain the existence of the earth without God. The Bible teaches a very different story and reveals an eyewitness account of the formation of the earth.

photosynthesize. Through photosynthesis, oxygen began to slowly accumulate in the atmosphere.

Another result of the volcanic gas was the collection of water vapor in the atmosphere. As the young atmosphere cooled, it released its water in the form of rain. As the rain fell on the hardening surface, the basins filled with water and the first seas were born. These seas then became the nursery for the first living organisms. The story above is described in the Prentice Hall text. On page 364 we read, ". . . Precambrian history is written in scattered, speculative episodes, like a long book with many missing pages." Then on pages 366–367 we read, ". . . Earth slowly cooled and the molten surface solidified into a crust. . . . the water vapor condensed to form clouds, and great rains began. . . . Torrential rains continued and slowly filled low areas, forming the oceans. . . . The first life forms on earth did not need oxygen."

So is this one of the pages recorded in great detail or one very detailed speculation? The description given is based on the assumption that the nebular hypothesis is true and that life actually evolved from nonliving chemicals. If the nebular hypothesis fails then all of the subsequent explanations fail. This chain of assumptions is present throughout the naturalistic explanations for the existence of the universe.

The lack of oxygen in the atmosphere is considered factual based on the assumption that life had not evolved to produce oxygen—a circular argument. The presence of oxygen is also a major problem for the chemical evolution of life from chemicals. Naturalistic scenarios for the origin of life on earth cannot accept oxygen on the early earth. Oxygen would have made it impossible for the organic molecules of life to form spontaneously—life could not have evolved from nonliving chemicals in the presence of oxygen. The textbooks claim that the rocks from the earliest periods of the earth do not contain evidence of oxygen in the atmosphere. To the contrary, there is no evidence in the sedimentary rocks that an oxygen-free atmosphere has existed at any time during the span of geological history. (See article 3:8 for more details.)

Figure 4 ▶ Earth's early atmosphere formed as volcanic eruptions released nitrogen, N_2; water vapor, H_2O; ammonia, NH_3; methane, CH_4; argon, Ar; sulfur dioxide, SO_2; and carbon dioxide, CO_2. **Holt 689**

Based on the assumption that the nebular hypothesis is correct, the cooling molten earth released its gases into the atmosphere. Volcanoes and gas pockets are believed to have formed the early atmosphere that changed over millions of years. The Bible records a different history with the earth's atmosphere created on Day Two.

To add to the problems, the ozone layer must have formed from atmospheric oxygen before the first organisms could have evolved to produce the oxygen that formed the ozone layer. These types of contradictions abound in the naturalistic explanations of life evolving on earth.

The last issue to deal with directly is the moon. The textbooks present a story of the collision of a Mars-sized object with the earth as the best explanation. The idea that the moon formed at the same time as the earth or that the moon was captured by the earth are mentioned as possibilities. The collision hypothesis is shown in detailed pictures that explain the process. The debris that was ejected from the impact eventually formed the new moon as it collected together.

The rocks that were collected from the moon from the *Apollo* missions are dated at 4.5 billion years using secular assumptions. This makes the moon just as old as the earth in the evolutionary story. The Bible gives similar ages for the earth and the moon as well. Both were created about 6,000 years ago and only three days apart. In Genesis 1:16 the "lesser light" is created to rule the night and give light on the earth. We can trust God's eyewitness account of how He did things over man's conjectures about the unseen past.

Claiming that the moon is 4.5 billion years old creates a major problem in the uniformitarian explanations. This is because the moon is slowly spiraling away from the earth at a current rate of 1.5 inches per year. That means that the moon was closer to the earth in the past. 6,000 years ago the moon would have been about 800 feet closer. Using the known rate of recession we can use calculus to determine the recession rate in the alleged distant past when the moon was much closer to the earth. This is necessary because when the moon is closer, the tidal bulges (and consequently the recession rate) are much larger. When we do the math properly, we calculate that the moon would have been touching the earth 1.5 billion years ago and would have been pulled apart before that by earth's gravity. This is just another confirmation that the earth and moon cannot possibly be 4.5 billion years old.

As we saw with the discussion of the big bang, there are many problems with the naturalistic explanations of the formation of our solar system. Many other problems are discussed in the articles that follow and the Tools for Digging Deeper. Because the naturalistic ideas are not based on the foundation of God's perfect Word, they fall short. Below is a table that summarizes the major differences discussed above. It is, at best, inconsistent to believe in the Bible as the inspired, infallible, sufficient Word of God and accept that the big bang and the nebular hypothesis are true. Because the two views contradict one another on many points, they cannot both be accurate without twisting, reordering, or compromising one or the other. Will you trust God's Word or man's reasoning when it comes to the formation of the solar system?

Table 3-1: Different Views on the Origin of the Solar System

Biblical View	Evolutionary View
6,000 years old	4.5 billion years old
Eyewitness account from the Creator	Theories based on the denial of a Creator
Earth created before the sun	Sun formed before the earth
Earth created before the stars	Stars formed before the earth
Earth created before the moon	Moon formed along with the earth
Earth began covered by water	Earth began as a molten ball
Seas were created on Day Three	Seas formed after millions of years as the earth cooled
The atmosphere was created on Day Two	The atmosphere evolved over billions of years
The earth was created by God to be inhabited (Isaiah 45:18)	Life on earth is a cosmic coincidence of the laws of nature

Reference Article Summaries

3:1 Pierre Simon Laplace: the nebular hypothesis, Parsons and Mackay, www.answersingenesis.org/creation/v3/i3/ideas.asp

Pierre Laplace was a brilliant scientist during the 1700s who worked in mathematics, chemistry, and astronomy. Laplace was also involved in standardizing measurement systems. Laplace recognized great order in the solar system and suggested that it should exist indefinitely if the sun did not change. His notions were intended to refute Newton's belief in a Divine Force holding all things together.

Laplace hypothesized that the solar system was the result of a spinning cloud of dust that spun off rings of gas which condensed to form the planets. The remaining gas became the sun. A modified version of this theory is currently promoted by many evolutionists, but there are many problems with this model. Laplace assumed that there was a spinning cloud that contracted, but the known laws of physics cannot explain how such a cloud could contract since the force from gas pressure far exceeds gravity under normal conditions. Other problems include the opposite rotation of Venus, Pluto, and Uranus, and the slow rotation of the sun compared to the rest of the angular momentum in the solar system.

Ultimately, Laplace's model is based on naturalistic assumptions that cannot explain the formation of the solar system—a system that is the result of design by God.

3:2 The heavens declare . . . a young solar system, Samec, www.answersingenesis.org/articles/am/v3/n1/heavens-declare-young-solar-system

Psalm 19 tells us that the heavens declare the glory of God. But what do the heavens declare about the age of the universe? Recent observations confirm that the universe is only a few thousand years old, as the Bible says.

A comet is a small, icy mass that orbits the sun and continually loses mass. The lost mass is seen as the two tails of a comet are blown off by the solar wind and the pressure of photons. Comets are also observed to break apart as they orbit near the sun and other planets. Since comets are constantly being eroded and destroyed, the solar system should contain no comets if it is truly 4.5 billion years old.

To combat this challenge, uniformitarian astronomers have imagined an Oort cloud that is 50,000 times farther from the earth than the sun. The Oort cloud is supposed to provide the solar system with long-period comets, though there is not a single shred of evidence for its existence. Short-period comets are alleged to come from the Kuiper belt, but the objects in this disk are different from comets and cannot adequately explain the existence of so many comets in our solar system.

Evolutionists would suggest that the moon has been dead for the last 3 billion years. However, frequent observations of color changes and luminous spots may indicate recent geologic activity. Since the moon is only thousands of years old, this activity is not unexpected.

Both Jupiter and Neptune give off about twice as much energy as they receive from the sun. If these planets were 4.5 billion years old, they would have cooled considerably or they must have an internal power source that could keep them hot for billions of years. Secular models suggest that the cores of these planets are undergoing nuclear fusion, but there are many problems with those models. The energy contained in these planets, and the other young-age indicators, confirm their young age and the biblical account of their creation.

3:3 First light from extrasolar planets, Lisle, www.answersingenesis.org/docs2005/0420extrasolar_planets.asp

The existence of planets around distant stars has been supported by the wobble produced as the planet orbits the star and the decrease in light from the star as the planet crosses in front of the star. Recently, astronomers have been able to measure the infrared energy from two of these planets, providing the first direct observation of extrasolar planets.

The extrasolar planets discovered so far do not fit the nebular hypothesis of planet formation. The planets located close to the stars are supposed to be small, rocky planets according to the evolutionary model. The planets that have been found are very large and orbit too near the stars to fit the secular expectations. These stellar systems continually remind us of the diversity and creativity that the Lord displayed on Day Four.

3:4 Uranus: the strange planet, Psarris, www.answersingenesis.org/creation/v24/i3/uranus.asp

Uranus is a planet about 64 times the volume of the earth that obits the sun at 19 times the distance. Uranus was discovered in 1781 but little was known about it until the Voyager 2 probe passed by it in 1986. At that time it was determined that the axis was tilted at 98 degrees to the ecliptic plane of the other planets' orbits. The tilt of the axis cannot be explained if Uranus formed from the spinning nebula that was the supposed origin of our solar system.

To explain the tilted axis, evolutionary astronomers claim that an earth-sized object must have struck Uranus to tilt it. This seems unlikely because Uranus has a very circular orbit that is very near the ecliptic plane—an impact would likely perturb the orbit. The small size of the moon and ring system, which are believed by evolutionists to be the remains of the impact, cannot account for the mass of the object that would cause the axis to tilt.

Invoking a catastrophe to explain the unnatural features of Uranus is a bit hypocritical as evolutionists often criticize biblical creationists for using the Flood to explain earth's features.

Uranus also radiates little heat into space, unlike similar-sized Neptune. If the two planets formed from the same process, we would expect them to have similar properties. Another discovery of the Voyager 2 probe is that the magnetic field axis is tilted 60 degrees from the rotational axis and is much stronger than expected. These characteristics cannot be explained by current evolutionary models, though Dr. Russell Humphreys used biblical assumptions to predict the field strength two years before it was known.

The many problems with the naturalistic explanation that are easily explained within the biblical framework make the creation of Uranus obvious.

3:5 Neptune: monument to creation, Psarris, www.answersingenesis.org/creation/v25/i1/neptune.asp

Neptune is a large gaseous planet that orbits the sun about 30 times farther than the earth. Little was known about Neptune until the Voyager 2 probe. Scientists did not find a cold, dead planet as they expected, but a planet with raging winds that gives off considerable heat. Another find of the probe was the tilted magnetic field with a strength that had been predicted by Dr. Russell Humphreys using biblical assumptions.

The Bible reveals that Neptune was created on Day 4, but evolutionists have no way of explaining the existence of Neptune and Uranus. According to the evolutionary nebular hypothesis, the planets are supposed to have formed from the disk of dust and gas that surrounded the forming sun about 4.5 billion years ago. As the dust cloud spun, the particles allegedly stuck to one another. As larger particles collided, planetesimals formed. The planetesimals continued to collide and eventually attracted gases to form the outer planets. But is this scenario possible?

Computer models of the nebular hypothesis have failed to show how such large planets can form so far from the sun. The time required is at least 10 billion years—double the supposed age of the solar system. This problem has been known for 30 years but it continues to be brushed aside in the media and textbooks because scientists "know" the solar system formed by itself. Despite the lack of a satisfactory explanation, they cling to models that reject the Creator and the evidence of His creation.

3:6 Evolution vs. creation: the order of events matters! Mortenson, www.answersingenesis.org/docs2006/0404order.asp

Many Christians believe that if we consider the days of creation in Genesis 1 as long ages we can harmonize the Bible with the big bang and the geological history promoted by scientists. This view is often called the "day-age" view and has many biblical problems. First, the text is intended to communicate that Creation occurred in six, 24-hour days. Second, this view requires millions of years of death and disease—consequences of the Curse after the Fall of mankind—before humans were on the earth.

The old-earth view of the creation of the universe also assumes that science has proven the true age of the earth and universe. In fact, science has only interpreted the evidence from radiometric dating, distant starlight, and the formation of rock layers.

Of highest importance is what is revealed in the text of Scripture about the order of events. Genesis 1 contradicts the evolutionary history of the universe and life in it at nearly every step. [See tables on page 52 and 77.] The Bible teaches that the earth was covered with water on Day One and at the time of the Flood while the evolutionary history denies that the earth was ever covered with water.

Because of the many contradictions, there is no way to harmonize the Bible with man's ideas about the evolution of the universe. We should trust the Word of God to reveal the truth about the events of Creation and earth's history.

3:7 The origin of life: a critique of current scientific models, Swee–Eng, www.answersingenesis.org/home/area/magazines/TJ/docs/tjv10n3_origin_life.pdf

This article provides an exhaustive discussion of the topics surrounding the origin of life. The discussion ranges from the presence of oxygen in the early atmosphere (despite the fact that it prohibits the formation of organic molecules) to the formation of DNA molecules and the complexity of the genetic code. Numerous evolutionary papers from scientific journals are used as evidence to support the idea that life could not have formed on earth by natural causes.

3:8 Did the early earth have a reducing atmosphere? Austin, www.icr.org/article/203

Evolutionists assume that the early earth lacked oxygen because life could not evolve in an environment containing oxygen. If this were true, the rocks older than 1.9 billion years should contain no evidence of being formed in an environment with oxygen. Iron deposits from these rock layers indicate an environment with oxygen. The lack of sulfide deposits and the presence of sulfates and other oxygen-bearing compounds also point to an oxidizing environment. These and other evidences point to an atmosphere that contained oxygen from its beginning.

3:9 Origin of the oceans, Sherwin, www.icr.org/article/99/13

Secular scientists have suggested that the oceans formed as rain slowly collected in basins after the molten earth cooled. The idea that this water was gathered from comets to fill the first oceans has been discredited by data from the Hale-Bopp comet. The comet was composed of deuterium-rich water. However, earth's oceans contain very little deuterium. The Bible explains that earth's oceans were created by God.

3:10 Lunar recession: does it support a young universe? Wright, www.answersingenesis.org/home/area/feedback/2006/0811.asp

Due to tidal forces, the moon is actually moving away from the earth at a current rate of one-and-a-half inches per year, but that rate changes as the distance changes. Calculating the distance between the earth and moon over time shows that the moon would have been touching the earth only 1.5 billion years ago—a big problem if the earth-moon system is 4.5 billion years old.

Even before that time, the earth would have been within the Roche Limit of earth's gravity and would have been pulled apart by earth's gravity. If the moon is only 6,000 years old, as the Bible teaches, there is no problem to overcome as the moon would have been a mere 800 feet closer.

3:11 Have scientists discovered the moon's origin? DeYoung, www.answersingenesis.org/Docs/399.asp

Evolutionary scientists have devised four major theories to explain the origin of the moon. The fission theory says that the moon split off from the spinning earth, but this is unlikely because the earth is spinning too slowly. The capture theory suggests that the moon was captured as it passed near the earth. However, it is more likely that this would throw the moon off into space and does not explain where the moon came from.

Another theory suggests that the earth and moon formed next to one another, but there is no explanation for how the particles came together in the first place. The final theory calls for a collision between the earth and another object. The debris caused by the impact formed the moon, but there are many problems to overcome with this model as well.

Despite man having traveled to the moon, there is still no satisfactory explanation of its origin from the evolutionary perspective. Scripture, however, clearly teaches that the moon was created suddenly by God.

3:12 Extraterrestrial bombardment of the inner solar system: a review with questions and comments based on new information, Froede, www.creationresearch.org/crsq/notes/38/38_4/Note0203.htm

As more information is gathered about impact events in the inner solar system, uniformitarian scientists believe that there was massive bombardment around 3.9 billion years ago. The source of the material for the bombardment is not clear but may have been from the Kuiper belt or Oort cloud but not likely from the asteroid belt.

From the creationist perspective, there is debate over how and when the bombardment began and what the source was. The bombardment may have been involved with the Flood, as many creation scientists have suggested. Comparing the cratering events on the moon and earth can help establish when the event occurred. There are several creationist models to consider, and they can be examined against the physical evidence and biblical framework. Despite the problems in the uniformitarian models, the asteroid belt may be the source of the materials, and the event happened in the last several thousand years rather than 3.9 billion years ago.

3:13 Comets and the age of the solar system, Faulkner, www.answersingenesis.org/tj/v11/i3/comets.asp

Comets are commonly used to argue that the solar system must be young. The basic argument is that comets loose material each time they orbit the sun, and there is a maximum of 11 million years for the orbit of a comet. Since comets are assumed to have formed from collapsing dust in the evolutionary models, the comets set a maximum age that is much younger than 4.5 billion years.

Comets are large chunks of ice and dust that are heated as they pass near the sun. The sun's radiation causes the coma to glow as particles are knocked off creating the two tails which always point away form the sun. The straight ion tail is created as gases are ionized by the solar wind. The curved tail is a trail of dust pushed outward by the solar radiation.

Comets have eccentric orbits and come in two types. Short-period comets have an orbital period of less than 200 years and usually orbit with the planets (prograde). Long-period comets have longer orbital periods and about half have a retrograde orbit that is opposite to the planets. Comets can also be lost by colliding with planets, as comet Shoemaker-Levi 9 did with Jupiter, or by being thrown out of the solar system by passing near a planet. If comets were part of the original solar system of 4.5 billion years ago, there should be none left in the solar system.

To solve this problem, evolutionists look to the Oort cloud and the Kuiper belt as the source for new comets. The Oort cloud is a hypothetical shell of comet nuclei that surrounds the solar system. It is supposed that the nuclei are occasionally perturbed and fall into the inner solar system to become long-period comets. The Kuiper belt is a doughnut-shaped region, beyond the orbit of Neptune. There have been many objects identified in this region and it is suggested that these objects are the source of short-period comets. However, the objects discovered in this region are much larger than comet nuclei. This challenges the assumption that the Kuiper belt is a source of new, short-period comets.

3:14 The solar system—new discoveries produce new mysteries, Gish, www.icr.org/article/62

If the solar system truly formed from a spinning nebula, we should see a high degree of similarity in the objects in the solar system. The sun contains 99% of the mass of the solar system but only 2% of its angular momentum. There must be a mechanism for transferring this momentum, but none has been rigorously demonstrated by evolutionary scientists. The axis of Uranus is tilted to 98° relative to its orbit around the sun. Many of its moons also orbit at its equator in the direction of rotation. These movements are the opposite that would be expected in the evolutionary model.

Phoebe, a moon of Saturn, and Triton, a moon of Neptune, orbit in a retrograde direction as do several of the moons of Jupiter. A group of three moons orbits Jupiter at

an angle of 30° from its equator—all contrary to evolutionary predictions.

The crust formations and magnetic field of Mercury
present problems for the evolutionary theory. Mercury is
too small to generate a magnetic field in the way the earth
is supposed to, so the model for earth's magnetic field is
not necessary to explain earth's magnetic field. The facts are
more consistent with a recent creation.

The moon Titan has a nitrogen-rich atmosphere which
contains hydrogen. This hydrogen could not be present
for billions of years on a small satellite, so the gas must
be constantly generated from within the moon through an
unknown process. And how such a small satellite formed
to retain methane, ammonia, and water is not understood.
Ultimately the composition of our solar system points to
the design of a Creator.

3:15 Saturn's rings short-lived and young, Snelling, www.
answersingenesis.org/tj/v11/i1/saturn.asp

The rings of Saturn have often been used by creationists to support a young age of the solar system. The rings
are too delicate to have existed for billions of years. Observations from 1695 to the present have confirmed that the
rings are shrinking. Recent data from the Hubble Space
Telescope has prompted evolutionists to suggest that the
rings may be as young as 30 million years old.

To create the young rings, it is suggested that a small
moon or passing comet was destroyed—an extremely
unlikely event. Despite the evolutionary interpretation of
the relatively young rings, the rings are a beautiful part of
God's creation.

**3:16 The young faint sun paradox and the age of the solar
system**, Faulkner, www.icr.org/article/429

Many characteristics combine to make life on earth
possible while the conditions on other planets make life
impossible. Mars has an extremely cold surface with no
liquid water known on the surface. Water is believed to

have once flowed on Mars's surface but it is hard to explain how this may have happened on such a cold planet.

Since the sun is powered by the fusion of hydrogen, it could burn for about ten billion years—about half of that time having already passed in the evolutionary view. As the composition of the core changes, so does the intensity of the light. The sun should be 40% brighter today than it was 4.5 billion years ago. This would impact the temperature of the planets. Evolutionists must explain how life evolved on a planet that would likely be frozen—an apparent paradox.

Changing atmospheric composition with a complex feedback system is generally used to explain how the paradox is avoided. As new forms of life evolved, the earth's atmosphere evolved along with it. The precise tuning of this process would have been nothing short of miraculous and has been called the Goldilocks syndrome.

Evolutionists have two ways to explain this. They can accept that it happened as a chance occurrence as the sun, atmosphere, earth, and living things all evolved together, or they can accept some type of guiding force that accomplished the task.

The third possibility is that the sun and earth are only thousands of years old and that there is no need to explain the paradox at all. If the earth and sun were recently created for life, there would be no conflict. The young faint sun paradox seems to rule out the idea that the solar system is billions of years old.

3:17 Proof of life evolving in the universe? White, www.answers-ingenesis.org/docs2001/0222news.asp

Many reports of water vapor and carbon compounds found near distant stars have led to claims that life must have evolved elsewhere in the universe. Evolutionists assume that there are planets similar to earth where life may have evolved, but they still cannot explain how life evolved on earth. The presence of conditions similar to earth does not prove that life has evolved elsewhere. The answer to the question of the origin of life is found in Genesis—the Creator made life on earth.

Questions to Consider

1. If there is no evidence to support the existence of the Oort cloud then how can it be considered a scientific hypothesis/theory?

2. How do scientists explain how a nebula collapses on itself when the laws of physics show that the heat and pressure would cause it to expand?

3. How do scientists explain the slow rotation of the sun with respect to the rest of the solar system?

4. What are the problems with the formation of the moon from an evolutionary perspective?

5. How can the retrograde rotation of planets and orbits of moons be explained in a naturalistic way?

6. Have the discoveries of extrasolar planetary systems confirmed the nebular hypothesis predictions?

Tools for Digging Deeper

Exploring Planet Earth by John Hudson Tiner

The New Answers Book by Ken Ham et al.

The New Answers Book 2 by Ken Ham et al.

Our Created Moon by Don DeYoung

Taking Back Astronomy by Jason Lisle

Universe by Design by Danny Faulkner

www.answersingenesis.org/go/astronomy

04

DATING METHODS

Knowing this first: that scoffers will come in the last days, walking according to their own lusts, and saying, "Where is the promise of His coming? For since the fathers fell asleep, all things continue as they were from the beginning of creation." For this they willfully forget: that by the word of God the heavens were of old, and the earth standing out of water and in the water, by which the world that then existed perished, being flooded with water.

2 Peter 3:3–6

What You Will Learn

Most scientists and many Christians believe that the radiometric dating methods prove that the earth is 4.5 billion years old. The textbooks speak of the radiometric dating techniques, and the dates themselves, as factual information. Far from being data, these dates are actually interpretations of the data. As discussed before, the assumptions influence the interpretation of the data. There are three main assumptions that must be made to accept radiometric dating methods. These must be accepted on faith in uniformitarian and naturalistic frameworks.

Recent research by a team of creation scientists known as the RATE (Radioisotopes and the Age of The Earth) group has demonstrated the unreliability of radiometric dating techniques. Even the use of isochron dating, which is supposed to eliminate some initial condition assumptions, produces dates that are not reliable. Despite the fact that there are many scientific problems with radiometric dating, there is a more significant problem. The Bible gives a much different picture and explains that relying on man's reasoning is foolishness. A fear of God and reverence for His Word is the beginning of wisdom. Starting with the Bible and developing a model for dating events in earth history will lead us to the truth. The Bible gives us a much more reliable history of the earth as it was recorded by God.

What Your Textbook Says about Dating Methods

Evolutionary Concept	Prentice Hall	Glencoe	Holt	Articles
Radioisotope dating shows the earth to be billions of years old.	39, T64C, 348–350, 354–355	387, 550, T552D, 562–563, T563, T578, 578–579, 648, T755, T769, T793	T183C– T183D, 193, 194–195, 212, T642, 642	4:1, 4:3, 5:1
Carbon-14 dating can be used to find the ages of some items.	T38, 350	563	196	4:2, 4:3, 5:1
Tree rings and varves can be used to date events, changes in the environment, and sediments.	351	564–565, 648	192, 641	4:4, 4:5

Note: Page numbers preceded by "T" indicate items from the teacher notes found in the margins of the Teacher's Edition.

What We Really Know about Dating Methods

When someone mentions scientific dating methods, the first thing to come to mind for most people is carbon dating. However, there are many methods that can be used to determine the age of the earth or other objects. The textbooks focus on relative dating, based on the layering of the rocks, and radiometric dating.

Relative ages are assigned to rocks based on the idea that rock layers lower in the strata were deposited before rock layers that are higher. Creationists do not necessarily disagree with this concept, but it can only be applied to layers that are found in one location and/or can be determined to have been deposited in a continuous layer over a very wide area. There is also a difference in the timescale used to explain the layers. Determining the relative age of a rock layer is based on the assumption that you know the ages of the rocks surrounding it. Uniformitarian geologists use so-called *absolute* dating methods to determine the ages of the surrounding rocks.

Certain types of rocks, especially those that form from magma (igneous), contain radioactive isotopes of different elements. It is possible to measure the ratio of the different radioactive parent isotopes and their daughter isotopes in a rock, but the ratios are not dates or ages. The dates must be inferred based on assumptions about the ratios. Some of the common isotope pairs used are K-Ar, Rb-Sr, Pb-Pb, and U-Pb.

Radiometric Dating: using ratios of isotopes produced in radioactive decay to calculate an age of the specimen based on assumed rates of decay and other assumptions.

Carbon-14 dating is another common technique, but it can only be used on carbon-containing things that were once alive. The method of calculating radiometric dates is like using an hourglass. You can use the hourglass to tell time if you know several things: the amount of sand in the top of the hourglass when it started flowing, the rate that the sand flows through the hole in the middle, and that the quantity of sand in each chamber has not been tampered with. If any of these three conditions is not accurately known, the hourglass will give an inaccurate measure of time.

Radiometric dating is based on the fact that radioactive isotopes decay to form isotopes of different elements. The starting isotope is called the parent and the end-product is called the daughter. The time it takes for one half of the parent atoms to decay to the daughter atoms is called the half-life. If certain things are known, it is possible to calculate the amount of time since the parent isotope began to decay. For example, if you began with 1 gram of carbon-14, after 5,730 years you would be left with 0.50 g and only 0.25 g after 11,460 years. The reason this age may not be a true age—even though it is commonly called an absolute age—is that it is based on several crucial assumptions. Most radiometric dating techniques must make three assumptions:

Using an hourglass to tell time is much like using radiometric dating to tell the age of rocks. There are key assumptions that we must accept in order for the method to be reliable.

1. The rate of radioactive decay is known and has been constant since the rock formed.

2. There has been no loss or gain of the parent or daughter isotopes from the rock.

3. The amounts of parent and daughter isotopes present when the rock formed are known.

The major problem with the first assumption is that there is no way to prove that the decay rate was not different at some point in the past. The claimed "fact" that decay rates have always been constant is actually an inference based on a uniformitarian assumption. It is true that radioisotope decay rates are stable today and are not largely affected by external conditions like change in temperature and pressure, but that does not mean that the rate has always been constant.

Recent research by a creation science group known as RATE (Radioisotopes and the Age of The Earth) has produced evidence of accelerated rates of decay at some point (or points) in the past. Creation scientists suggest that there are two possible times that God supernaturally intervened on a global scale—during Creation Week and the Flood. It is not unreasonable to assume that God used the energy of accelerated radioactive decay to initiate and drive the major geologic changes in the earth that accompanied the Flood.

Evidence for the period of accelerated decay is found in zircon crystals. Zircon crystals in granite contain radioactive uranium-238, which decays into lead over time. As the uranium decays, helium is produced in the crystals. Helium escapes from the crystals at a known, measurable rate. If those rocks were over a billion years old, as evolutionists claim, the helium should have leaked out of the rock. The presence of lots of helium in the crystals is evidence in support of a young earth.

Other important findings of the RATE project include detecting carbon-14 in coal and diamonds. If these substances were really millions or billions of years old respectively, there should be no carbon-14 left in them. Carbon-14 has a half-life of 5,730 years. With the most accurate mass spectrometers, the oldest calculated *age* of items containing carbon-14 is about 80,000 years. Diamonds are assumed to be many billions of years old and should contain no detectable carbon-14 as it would have all decayed to nitrogen-14 long ago. The same is true of coal which was supposedly deposited

Fossils and rocks do not come with dates stamped on them. The dates must be interpreted based on the evidence. Biblical geologists start with the assumptions laid out in the Bible and conclude that the rocks must be less than 6,000 years old. Evolutionists reject the authority of the Bible and conclude that the rocks must be millions or billions of years old.

hundreds of millions of years ago, according to the evolutionary model. The presence of carbon-14 in these materials clearly supports the idea of a young earth as described by the Bible.

The assumption that there has been no loss or gain of the isotopes in the rock (assumption 2) does not take into account the impact of weathering by surface and ground waters and the diffusion of gases. It is impossible to know to what degree the parent and daughter products have been added to or removed from the rocks over the alleged millions or billions of years.

The final assumption (assumption 3) does not take into account the fact that isotopes can be inherited from the source areas of magmas and/or from surrounding rocks as the magmas pass through the mantle and crust of the earth. Uniformitarian geologists do make efforts to eliminate errors, but the fact that rocks of known recent age give dates of millions, and even billions, of years supports the claim that radiometric dating cannot provide accurate "absolute" dates. Also, samples taken a few feet apart can give ages that differ by many hundreds of millions of years.

Many people do not realize that fossils themselves are usually not directly dated. Instead, layers that contain datable igneous rocks above or below a fossil-bearing layer are used to estimate the age of the fossil. The age of the fossil can be estimated within the range of the layers above and below it. In some cases, the ages are correlated to other rock layers of supposedly known age or by using index fossils. These methods assume that the distribution of index fossils and the correlation of strata are well understood on a global scale.

Another finding of the RATE team is very intriguing. The team took samples of diabase, an igneous rock, and tested them using various radiometric dating techniques. If the dating methods are all objective and reliable, then they should give similar dates. The rocks were tested as whole-rock samples using K-Ar dating and also separated into individual minerals. The whole-rock and separated mineral samples allow a method known as isochron dating to be done. This method is supposed to eliminate the assumption that the initial concentration of the daughter element is zero.

Despite removing this assumption, the RATE team has shown that this method is not reliable. Dating the Cardenas Basalt, a layer near the bottom of Grand Canyon, and a volcanic layer from near the top of Grand Canyon produced an amazing result. Based on

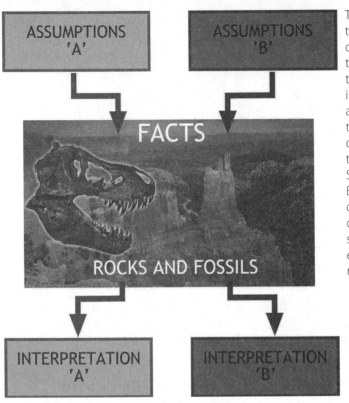

ASSUMPTIONS 'A'

ASSUMPTIONS 'B'

FACTS

ROCKS AND FOSSILS

INTERPRETATION 'A'

INTERPRETATION 'B'

The facts from the rock layers do not speak for themselves—they must be interpreted. The assumptions used to interpret the data influence the conclusion. Starting with the Bible produces different conclusions than starting with evolutionary reasoning.

the law of superposition, the lower layers in the canyon should be older than the upper layers (unless there was an intrusion or other event that changed the order). Using isochron dating from a respected lab, the lower rocks were dated at 1.07 billion years and the upper, and presumably younger rocks, were dated at 1.34 billion years. There is an obvious discordance (disagreement) in the data. So the question becomes, "Can we trust the dates given in the textbooks if the techniques are not objective?" (More information on the RATE research can be found in article 4:3.)

Because these dates are based on methods with multiple assumptions, and are contrary to the Bible, we must reject that they are accurate. Despite the fact that a majority of scientists and even many theologians accept the dates, God's Word must be our ultimate authority.

There are many other methods that can be used to establish ages for parts of the earth and the solar system. These methods will be discussed in the following chapter. Regardless of what method we use, we must start with assumptions and interpret the facts accordingly. Understanding what those assumptions are is important. If we are not aware of the assumptions that are being used, we can easily be deceived. We should always start with the Bible, the ultimate source of truth.

When we try to use man's ideas and assumptions to understand nature, we are forgetting that Proverbs 2:1–6 tells us:

> My son, if you receive my words, and treasure my
> commands within you,
> So that you incline your ear to wisdom, and apply
> your heart to understanding;
> Yes, if you cry out for discernment, and lift up your
> voice for understanding,
> If you seek her as silver, and search for her as for
> hidden treasures;
> Then you will understand the fear of the Lord, and
> find the knowledge of God.

Reference Article Summaries

4:1 Does radiometric dating prove the earth is old? Riddle, www.answersingenesis.org/articles/nab/does-radiometric-dating-prove

Proponents of evolution suggest that radiometric dating has proven that the earth is between 4.5 and 4.6 billion years old. But what is this age based on? A straightforward reading of the Bible shows that the earth was created in six days about 6,000 years ago. Radiometric dating uses ratios of isotopes in rocks to infer the age of the rock.

Scientists use a mix of observational data and assumptions about the past to determine the radiometric age of a rock. Comparing the amount of a parent isotope to the amount of its daughter isotope and knowing the rate of change from parent into daughter (known as the half-life), the age of the rock can be determined. However, there are several assumptions that must be made in this process.

The three critical assumptions are:

1. The initial conditions of the rock sample are accurately known.

2. The amount of parent or daughter elements in a sample has not been altered by processes other than radioactive decay.

3. The decay rate (or half–life) of the parent isotope has remained constant since the rock was formed.

An hourglass can be used as an analogy to explain the assumptions. An hourglass can be used to tell time only if we know how much sand was in each chamber at the beginning, that there was no sand added or removed from either chamber, and that the sand falls at a constant rate. If any of these factors is not known, the time given may not be accurate. The same goes for the dating of rocks using radioisotopes. Assumption 1 was proven false when scientists from the RATE group had rocks of known age dated. These rocks were dated at up to 3.5 million years old when none of them were older than 70 years. How can we trust this method to tell us the age of rocks when the data do not match with observations?

Isochron dating is supposed to remove the assumption of initial conditions, but some different assumptions are necessary. If radiometric dating techniques are objective and accurate, then comparing the single–sample dates to the isochron dates should give similar results. In the RATE report there were dates that differed by up to a billion years. One volcanic rock layer from the top of Grand Canyon was dated 270 million years older than the oldest rocks below it near the bottom of the canyon.

Other case studies by the RATE group show dates that vary greatly depending on the sample and dating technique used. The most reasonable explanation seems to be that the rates of decay have been different at some point in the past. This is supported by the presence of large amounts of helium in some minerals. If there had been more than a billion years since the rocks had formed, the helium should have leaked out of the rocks by now. The presence of helium seems to support the recent accelerated decay of the isotopes, leaving a large amount of helium trapped in the rocks.

The Bible presents a very different picture of the age of the earth when compared to radiometric dating using evolutionary assumptions. It is better to use the infallible Word of God for our scientific assumptions than to compromise it with man's ideas.

4:2 Doesn't carbon-14 dating disprove the Bible? Riddle, www. answersingenesis.org/articles/nab/does-c14-disprove-the-bible

Radiometric dating is a technique that uses the change of one isotope, the parent, to another, the daughter, to determine the amount of time since the decay began. Carbon-14 is supposed to allow dating of objects up to 60,000 years. If these dates were true, they would seem to discredit the biblical account of a young earth of about 6,000 years.

Since the Bible is the inspired Word of God, we should examine the validity of the standard interpretation of carbon-14 dating by asking several questions:

1. Is the explanation of the data derived from empirical, observational science, or an interpretation of past events (historical science)?

2. Are there any assumptions involved in the dating method?

3. Are the dates provided by carbon-14 dating consistent with what we observe?

4. Do all scientists accept the carbon-14 dating method as reliable and accurate?

Carbon-14 dating is used to date things that were once living. The unstable carbon-14 decays to stable nitrogen-14 as one of its protons is converted to a neutron through beta decay. Carbon-14 is constantly supplied as high energy neutrons collide with nitrogen-14 in the upper atmosphere. This carbon-14 combines with oxygen to form carbon dioxide and is taken in by plants and then animals. Each living thing should have roughly the same ratio of radioactive carbon-14 to normal carbon-12.

When an organism dies, it no longer takes in carbon-14, and the decay process begins. Assuming that the rate of decay and the starting amount of carbon-14 is known, this decay process can be used as a clock. However, the ratio of carbon isotopes is not constant and can be affected by the earth's magnetic field strength and the amount of plant and animal matter in the biosphere. The plants and animals buried in the recent Flood could account for a large change in the ratios and demonstrate the false assumption of carbon equilibrium.

The RATE group has also documented carbon-14 in coal and diamonds that are supposed to be millions to billions of years old. If these items were truly more than 100,000 years old, there should be no detectable carbon-14 present in them. These findings point to the age of the earth being much younger than evolutionary scientists would suggest.

4:3 Radioisotopes and the age of the earth, Snelling, www. answersingenesis.org/articles/am/v2/n4/radioisotopes-earth

A long-term research project involving several creation scientists has produced intriguing new evidence in support of an earth that is thousands of years old rather than many billions. Some of the findings are summarized below.

The presence of fission tracks and radiohalos in crystals demonstrates that hundreds of millions of years worth of radioactive decay has occurred in a very short period. Because the Bible indicates the earth is young (about 6,000 years old), this large quantity of nuclear decay must have occurred at much faster rates than those measured today.

Using various radiometric dating methods to measure the ages of rock samples consistently produced ages that varied greatly. This may be explained by the different parent atoms having decayed at different rates in the past—an explanation not allowed by evolutionists. These changes in decay rates could be accounted for by very small changes in the binding forces within the nuclei of the parent atoms.

Research has been done to demonstrate that many of

the assumptions used in radiometric dating are false. Starting from biblical assumptions regarding the Flood and Creation can provide a new framework for interpreting current scientific data.

4:4 Tree rings and biblical chronology, Lorey, www.icr.org/article/381

Bristlecone pines are the oldest living things on the earth. Native to the mountains of California and Nevada, the oldest tree has been dated at 4,600 years old. By correlating the rings with dead wood found near the trees and beams from local buildings, a chronology of 11,300 rings has been suggested. However, this does not necessarily correlate to years because multiple rings can grow in one year.

The 4,600 year age of the oldest tree, named Methuselah, corresponds to the date of the Flood given by Ussher and others. If Methuselah began growing shortly after the Flood, then it stands as a record that confirms the Bible.

4:5 Are there half a million years in the sediments of Lake Van? Oard, www.answersingenesis.org/articles/am/v2/n2/lake-van-rhythmites

Lake Van is a salt lake in Turkey that uniformitarian scientists believe holds a record of the last 800,000 years of the earth's climate. The layers of sediment are up to 400 meters thick and were supposedly laid down one layer at a time each year. Evolutionists assume the layers, called varves, roughly correspond to years based on assumptions about present processes.

Varves are also used to date other lakes around the world to the time of the last ice age—supposedly 10,000 years ago. Many other alleged varve deposits challenge the biblical timescale and must be reinterpreted within the creationist framework. The repeating layers should be referred to as rhythmites and simply represent successive deposits over time. These different layers can be deposited as particles of different size and density settle out of flowing water. Studies at Lake Walensee, Switzerland, showed over 300 layers forming in 160 years. Different areas had different patterns and were not able to be correlated directly.

Other studies have shown multiple layers forming as the result of light rainfall, increasing river flow, and increased snowmelt. Underwater turbidity currents are often interpreted as varves, but they form many layers rapidly. It is common, therefore, for multiple layers to form in a single year.

All of these layers can be explained within the Flood model as catastrophic melting and drainage events deposited many layers over a short period of time during localized residual catastrophism in the immediate aftermath of the Flood. Uniformitarian geologists assume the slow rate of deposition as observed today for the past. However, in many cases they really have not observed the present sedimentation rate, and in some cases where they have used sediment traps, not all the deposition has been recorded. Creationists, on the other hand, can postulate much higher rates in the past due to the Flood, localized residual post-Flood catastrophism, and/or a rapid post-Flood Ice Age— the rate tapering off to the present slow rate.

Questions to Consider

1. Do radiometric dating techniques always show that rocks lower in the geologic layers are older than rocks that are higher?

2. If radiometric dating on rocks known to be only a few years old yields dates of millions of years, why should we trust that the techniques can be used to accurately date rocks of unknown ages?

3. In radiometric dating techniques, how do we know how much parent material the sample started with? How do we know none of the parent or daughter isotope was added or removed? How do we know the decay rate is constant?

4. When items are carbon-14 dated, how do we know how much carbon-14 was initially present in the sample? Could the ratio of carbon-14 to carbon-12 have been different at different times in earth's history? How can scientists accurately adjust their calculations if the isotope ratios were never observed and recorded?

5. What assumptions are involved in radiometric dating?

Tools for Digging Deeper

Evolution: The Fossils Still Say No! by Duane Gish

The Geology Book by John Morris

The New Answers Book by Ken Ham et al.

The New Answers Book 2 by Ken Ham et al.

Radioisotopes and the Age of the Earth Volume 1 (Technical) by ICR

Radioisotopes and the Age of the Earth Volume 2 (Technical) by ICR

Thousands . . . Not Billions by Don DeYoung

www.answersingenesis.org/go/dating

05

AGE OF THE SOLAR SYSTEM

Then God said, "Let there be lights in the firmament of the heavens to divide the day from the night; and let them be for signs and seasons, and for days and years; and let them be for lights in the firmament of the heavens to give light on the earth"; and it was so. Then God made two great lights: the greater light to rule the day, and the lesser light to rule the night. He made the stars also.

Genesis 1:14–16

What You Will Learn

Evolutionists and young earth creationists both agree that the earth is about the same age as the solar system. Evolutionists believe that both formed spontaneously about 4.5 billion years ago. Young-earth creationists believe that the earth was formed on Day One and the rest of the solar system and universe on Day Four. Ultimately, these two positions are based on foundational beliefs— man's authority versus God's authority. Evolutionary scientists start with man's ideas about the age of the earth and build their theories around a set of starting assumptions. These assumptions are then used to interpret the data from the different dating techniques that can be used to estimate the ages of the earth. The most popular of these methods uses radioactive isotopes to calculate the age of rocks, but there are other methods that do not agree with the interpretation of radiometric data. These other methods are often ignored or explained away by evolutionists.

Young earth creationists point to dating techniques that put a limit on the age of the earth and solar system. These methods include the strength of the earth's magnetic field, the amount of salt in the ocean, the history of human civilizations, and others to confirm the biblical models and show that the evolutionary models cannot be accurate. These methods establish a maximum age for many earth and space systems that is much too small to confirm the evolutionary age of 4.5 billion years.

From a biblical perspective, any dates that extend beyond 6,000 years must be rejected. When considering life on earth, including human cultures and artifacts, we must also consider the Flood of 4,300 years ago. Cave paintings made 15,000 years ago are presented as fact in the textbooks, but these dates cannot be accepted as truth according to the ultimate standard—the Bible.

What Your Textbook Says about the Age of the Solar System

Evolutionary Concept	Prentice Hall	Glencoe	Holt	Articles
People used to believe the earth was 6,000 years old but science has shown it formed 4.6 billion years ago.	T1C, 2, T306C–D, 336–337, 347, 350	6, 385, 387, 557, T563, 570–571, T576, 578–579, T581, 581–582, 610, T662, 648, T686	27, 35, 185, 216–217	4:1, 4:3, 5:1, 5:2, 5:3, 5:4
Human history goes back tens of thousands of years.	T354	T384C, 385, T654, T654C, T678, 715	226, T406, T417D, T657D	5:1, 5:2, 5:3, 5:4, 5:5, 5:6, 5:7
Earth's processes (magnetic field, climate, energy/matter, volcanic activity, continent formation, ocean salinity, precession, etc.) indicate that it is very old.	20–21, 94, T156C, T278D, 287, 423, T586D, T600, 602, 657, 664–665	234, 359, 393–395, T395C, 471, 481, T490, 565, T654D, 657, 679, 686, T697, 740–741, T783, 783	36, 155, 173, T237D, T244, 244–245, 257, 259, 291, 338, T469D, 548, 740, T777	5:1, 9:1

Note: Page numbers preceded by "T" indicate items from the teacher notes found in the margins of the Teacher's Edition.

What We Really Know about the Age of the Solar System

If you were to ask most people how we determine the age of the earth and the solar system you would probably hear something about radiometric dating of rocks. Although this is one way that evolutionary scientists interpret the age of the earth, there are many other techniques that can be used. Both evolutionists and biblical creationists would agree that the earth and the solar system are about the same age—the actual age of each is where they disagree.

Other methods can be used to date events in the history of the solar system. Using lunar recession, we established a limit of 1.5 billion years on the age of the moon (see chapter 3). This does not mean that the solar system is that old, but that it cannot be older than that. Since the biblical age of 6,000 years falls within that age and the evolutionary age of 4.5 billion years is well beyond that limit, this dating technique confirms the biblical model as a reasonable answer. The moon was created very near its present position

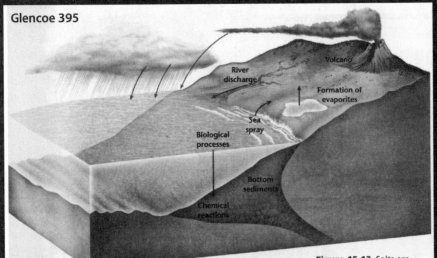

Glencoe 395

Despite the evolutionists' claim that the salinity of the ocean is constant, there is no physical mechanism to support the claim. Of the known inputs and outputs of salt only about 25% of sodium can be shown to leave the oceans. This limits the age of the oceans to 62 million years—a problem for evolutionists.

Figure 15-13 Salts are added to seawater by volcanic eruptions and by the weathering and erosion of rocks. Salts are removed from seawater by the formation of evaporites and biological processes. Salty droplets also are deposited inland by winds.

and has moved away from the earth in the last 6,000 years.

The amount of salt in the oceans is another way to set a limit on the age of the earth's oceans. In the evolutionary model, the seas formed over 4 billion years ago. Salt has been accumulating in the oceans as salts flow into the oceans from rivers. Evolutionists claim that the sodium content is in a steady-state "because salts are removed from the ocean at the same rate as they are added" (Glencoe, p. 394). This is a false statement. Only about 25% of the sodium can be shown to be leaving the ocean. Knowing the rates of sodium input and output, the maximum age of the oceans can be calculated at 62 million years. Again, this does not fit within a billions-of-years explanation.

Within the biblical creation model, we can explain the relatively high concentration of sodium and other salts in the seas. If the earth were only 6,000 years old and we assumed that the change in salinity has been constant, the seas would contain much less salt than they do. However, we cannot forget that there was a global Flood about 4,300 years ago. As the Flood ripped up the surface of the earth, much mineral content would have been dissolved in the water that would eventually become today's seas.

It is also impossible to know how salty the seas were at the time of their creation. More salt would have been transported to the seas as the water flowed off of the continents. Later, reservoirs (like the one that formed Grand Canyon) released their water and dissolved salts into the ocean basins. Starting with the history of the Bible, we can explain the present conditions of the oceans better than if we start from evolutionary assumptions and uniformitarian principles.

Other dating methods put a limit on the age of the earth and the solar system. Earth's magnetic field is becoming weaker. Evolutionists have created a hypothesis to explain the cyclical nature of the direction of the earth's magnetic field. This hypothesis has many problems and maintains that the field takes hundreds of thousands of years to reverse. The zebra-striped pattern of magnetism in the spreading sea floor is used as evidence that the ocean basins are many millions of years old. This will be discussed in more detail in chapter 9.

Evidence from lava flows has shown a rapid change of 45° in the magnetic field direction over a 15-day period. Creationists explain this as fluctuation during the catastrophic events of the

Flood period, while evolutionists have great difficulty explaining such rapid changes.

Indicators of the youthfulness of the solar system, and therefore the earth, are the intricate rings of Saturn and Uranus, and the large amounts of heat given off by planets like Jupiter. The presence of comets and other evidences discussed in chapter 3 confirm the biblical teaching of a young earth and solar system.

The textbooks, as well as any other source of evolutionary content, use the word *prehistoric* when referring to events that allegedly occurred before recorded history. Fossils are often described as being from prehistoric times as is art found in caves and the development of agriculture. The idea of prehistoric men hunting prehistoric animals is not a biblically sound idea. As Genesis is a record of the earth and universe from "the beginning," there could not have been anything that existed before the beginning—aside from God. So there could have been nothing before recorded history. Based on this argument, the term *prehistoric* is unbiblical. We may consider things to be ancient if they are thousands of years old, but there has never existed a time during which written records have not been kept.

When Adam was created on Day Six, he had the ability to communicate with God and Eve. The ability to name the many animals that he named demonstrates his intellect and command of language. With such intellect, why would we accept that he was not able to write as well? His grandsons are noted for their skills in metalworking and music, so it is natural to assume that they could record ideas in written form. Any records kept before the Flood would have been lost, except for those that Noah could have very easily preserved aboard the Ark. Though the earliest known written records come from the period shortly after the Flood, there is no biblical reason to doubt that these ancient men and women could read and write. We cannot rightly call events, peoples, and artifacts prehistoric because the highlights of human history are recorded from the beginning of time.

How, exactly, do we arrive at the dates that should be assigned to events that are both historic and allegedly prehistoric? The answer is to look to the Bible as the primary source of truth. Since the Bible is the inspired Word of God, we can trust its history. When we look at the Bible, we see that the earth is only about 6,000 years old—a claim that evolutionists must deny.

CREATIONWISE

Although man's ideas about the age of the earth continue to change, God's Word remains a constant source of truth.

The 6,000-year age of the earth is quite simple to glean from the Bible, though there is no passage that says exactly how old the earth is. We know that there have been roughly 2,000 years between the present and the birth of Christ. There were approximately 2,000 years between Christ and Abraham, and then the Bible gives detailed genealogies from Abraham to Adam. Genesis 5 and 11 provide chronological genealogies that, through some simple addition, provide another 2,000 years between Adam and Abraham. Combining these three periods of human history, we arrive at the biblical age of approximately 6,000 years.

Knowing the biblical age of the earth, we can compare the dates given in the textbooks and other sources. Any dates beyond 6,000 years must be incorrect interpretations of the evidence. One example is the dating of cave art to 15,000 years ago. Since the caves were formed after the Flood, these drawings cannot be older than about 4,300 years. Likewise, any cultures or their artifacts cannot be older than the dispersion at Babel. This event happened after the Flood and before Abraham, or around 4,200 years ago. The inflated ages given to these ancient cultures are based on evolutionary and uniformitarian assumptions. These faulty assumptions lead to faulty dates.

Just as we cannot accept dates for events on earth that extend beyond 6,000 years, neither can we accept dates of billions of years for the formation of the earth and the solar system. Ultimately, the age of the earth and the solar system are based on beliefs. Believing that evolutionary science can answer the question leads many to an age of 4.5 billion years. Believing in the Bible as the source for truth leads to a radically different conclusion—an earth which is 6,000 years old.

Reference Article Summaries

5:1 Evidence for a young world, Humphreys, www.answersin-genesis.org/docs/4005.asp

Fourteen natural phenomena are presented that demonstrate the young age of the earth. Many natural processes can be used to set a maximum age of the earth. This article explains each of the methods and the maximum age calculated—all of which show that the earth is too young to have formed 4.5 billion years ago.

The dating methods include the following: galaxies that wind themselves up too fast, too few supernova remnants, short-lived comets, too little sea floor mud, too little sodium in the sea, earth's strong magnetic field, tightly bent strata, intact DNA in fossils, radiohalos, helium in minerals, carbon-14 in deep layers, too few Stone Age skeletons, the recent development of agriculture, and the short history of written records. These evidences, along with many others, support the biblical age of the earth—a young age of 6,000 years.

5:2 The world: born in 4004 BC? Pierce, www.answersingenesis.org/articles/am/v1/n1/world-born-4004-bc

The age of the earth is a very contentious issue, and Christians are often mocked for believing the earth is only 6,000 years old. This age had been widely accepted by Christians, and Archbishop Ussher's date of 4004 BC was a respectable attempt at formulating the biblical age of the earth's creation. The date came into doubt when people began to trust secular dating methods over the Bible.

Ussher used the Bible as the basis for his calculations, supplementing his research with other historical records, but always giving the Bible supremacy. Ussher went so far as to suggest that Day One of Creation Week was on October 23, 4004 BC. This might seem like a stretch, but Ussher used sound reasoning to arrive at his date. Though we can not know for sure that Ussher's date is accurate, it is certainly a reasonable date based on a plain reading of Scripture. With roughly 2,000 years since Christ, about 2,000 years between Christ and Abraham, and just over 2,000 years between Adam and Abraham, the biblical record clearly points to a 6,000 year old earth.

5:3 Why shouldn't Christians accept millions of years?
Mortenson, www.answersingenesis.org/articles/nab/why-christians-shouldnt-accept-millions

For the first 1,800 years of church history almost all Christians believed in an earth created in six literal days about 4,000 years before Christ and that it was devastated by a global Flood. About 200 years ago the idea of long ages was popularized, and many in the church started accepting the opinion of man over the Word of God. The new views include a gap in Genesis, reinterpreting the days to mean long ages (day-age view), a local rather than a global Flood, the framework hypothesis, God-directed theistic evolution, and progressive creationism.

Those holding to the traditional view are referred to as young–earth creationists as all of the other positions accept an earth much older than 6,000 years. Many suggest that promoting a young earth hinders the message of the gospel and causes division in the church. However, compromising the text of the Bible to accommodate man's ideas is much more dangerous.

Biblical support for the days of creation being 24 hour days is abundant. The Hebrew word *yom* means a 24-hour day in the vast majority of its uses and clearly within the context of morning and evening indicates a normal day. Exodus 20:11 confirms this idea as the Sabbath rest commandment is tied to Creation week. The 6,000-year age is clear from the genealogies given in Genesis 5 and 11 and other chronological information in the

AFTER EDEN
by Dan Lietha

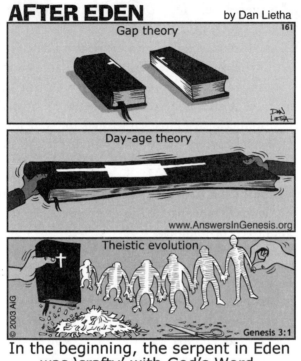

In the beginning, the serpent in Eden
was 'crafty' with God's Word.
Since then, we've been crafty too.

Bible. Jesus's own words from Mark 10:6 confirm that Adam and Eve were made at the "beginning of creation," not billions of years later.

Noah's Flood was clearly a global event accompanied by earthquakes, tsunamis, and volcanoes as the water covered all of the high hills and mountains. The layers of rock containing billions of fossils are a testimony to this catastrophe. Radiometric dating of the layers is generally used to discredit the evidence supporting a global Flood in recent history, but those dating methods involve many assumptions and are based on anti-biblical ideas.

One of the most important points to consider is that the Bible clearly teaches that death is the result of sin. Belief in millions of years requires the death of billions of animals and the presence of disease and suffering in animals before Adam had sinned. Would God call a world "very good" if it contained such things? This makes God a bumbling, cruel creator who uses disease, natural disasters, and extinctions to advance life on earth while still calling it "very good."

The biblical record makes it clear that the idea of millions and billions of years of earth history is not compatible with Christianity.

5:4 Meeting the ancestors, Grigg, www.answersingenesis.org/creation/v25/i2/ancestors.asp

It is interesting to think that Lamech, Noah's father, could have talked with Adam about life in the Garden of Eden and that Abraham could have talked with Shem about life on the Ark. This is possible because the Bible meticulously records the ages of these patriarchs and their ages when their sons were born. By simple arithmetic, we can arrive at the age of the earth based on these genealogies.

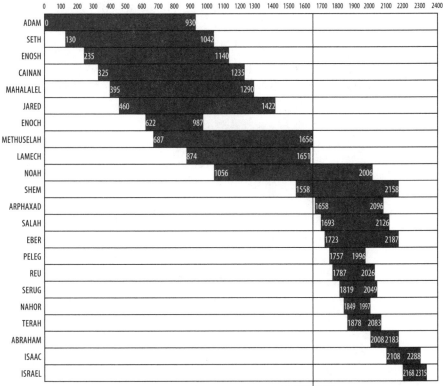

FLOOD 1656

The specific dates given with each of these men make it impossible to insert large gaps in the history of Genesis.

These dates also allow us to accurately date the Flood at 1,656 years after God created the earth. It is often claimed by skeptics of a young earth that there are gaps or inaccuracies in the records. However, the details given, and the fact that the genealogies are repeated in 1 Chronicles and Luke 3, indicate these are precise, literal records. In the book of Jude we also read that Enoch was the seventh from Adam, just as we see in the Genesis 5 record. These ideas all reinforce that the genealogies give a record we can trust as an accurate, literal history.

5:5 Egypt or Babel: which came first? Wise, www.answersin-genesis.org/articles/am/v3/n2/egypt-or-babel

Many nations and cultures throughout history have claimed that they are the oldest nation. Historians have constructed chronologies to prove their claims, but the dates ultimately point to one pivotal event—the elusive date of the division at Babel. From the Bible, we can determine that the events of Babel happened between the Flood and the call of Abraham, but the exact date is unknown.

The nations were likely divided during the lifetime of Peleg (Genesis 10:25), who was born 101 years after the Flood and died 239 years after the Flood. This biblical time frame does not fit with the king lists of the Egyptians and Sumerians. However, these lists include kings who supposedly lived for thousands of years and overlapping ruling periods are listed as sequential. There are also different lists using different numbers of kings. The result is inflated genealogies when compared to the Bible.

Records of astronomical events also demonstrate that the non-biblical lists are inflated. Our current understanding of celestial movements allows us to determine when these events occurred, and it is clear that the record keepers extended their chronologies. This was most likely done to promote their culture and leaders over others. These records also fail to mention the division of languages. This would suggest that they were written after that event and that the record found in the Bible is the most reliable for dating Babel.

5:6 The sixteen grandsons of Noah, Hunt and Grigg, www. answersingenesis.org/creation/v20/i4/noah.asp

After the Flood, the earth was repopulated by Noah's three sons, who had a total of sixteen sons of their own as recorded in Genesis 10. After the dispersion at Babel, these grandsons were spread across the globe and founded nations in the areas they settled.

Many ancient cultures worshipped their ancestors, and the names of many regions, physical features, and people groups can be traced back to one of the sixteen grandsons. Of the seven sons of Japheth, the Gomerites can be traced to Western Europe. The Welsh language is called Gomeraeg, and Welsh history records the landing of the descendants of Gomer 300 years after the Flood. Many other names can be traced through history back to one of these seven sons and their descendants as they settled throughout Europe and western Asia.

Of the four sons of Ham, Phut is the Hebrew name for Libya, Cush is the name for Ethiopia, and Mizraim the word for Egypt. The fourth son, Canaan, is the namesake of the region known as Palestine today—the biblical land of the Canaanites and Philistines.

From the five sons of Shem we can also identify where their descendants settled. Elam is the ancient name for Persia, the area we know as Iran today. Asshur is the Hebrew word for the Assyrians, and history records that he was worshipped by his descendants. Eber, a descendant of Arphaxad, gave his name to the Hebrew people, while Lydia, now western Turkey, bears the ancestry of Lud. Aramaic is the language of the Syrians, a group that can be traced to Aram.

Looking only briefly at the grandsons of Noah makes it clear that these were historical individuals who founded the earliest civilizations after the Flood.

5:7 Taking a bead on an old earth, www.answersingenesis.org/
articles/am/v3/n1/taking-a-bead

A dozen seashell necklaces (or perhaps bracelets) were discovered in a cave in Morocco, North Africa. The discovery surprised archaeologists who dated the ornamental jewelry at 82,000 years old, but previously believed that humans had not developed such art until around 50,000 years ago.

Dating such discoveries has led some Christians to wonder when God created humans. Many "progressive creationists" have gradually pushed their range of dates back: 10,000–25,000 years, then 10,000–35,000, up to 60,000, and sometimes up to 100,000 years.

A clear reading of Genesis, on the other hand, shows that mankind was created about 6,000 years ago, but all vestiges of the earliest cultures were destroyed during the Flood. These artifacts, found in post-Flood geologic formations, must be less than 4,300 years old. The dating methods of secular archaeologists are based on incorrect assumptions, and the key to correct dates is the infallible Word of God.

Questions to Consider

1. How many different ways are there to calculate the age of the earth and its systems? Why don't they all agree? How do we know which is correct?

2. How can we explain the relatively sudden appearance of advanced civilizations about 10,000 years ago if humans have been around for 100–200,000 years?

3. Why do scientists reject the Bible as an accurate record of the past, when there are so many archaeological finds confirmed by the Bible?

4. If the scientific age of the earth has changed many times in the past, why should we trust the dates given in the textbooks today? How old were you taught the earth was when you were in high school/college?

Tools for Digging Deeper

The New Answers Book by Ken Ham et al.

The New Answers Book 2 by Ken Ham et al.

Radioisotopes and the Age of the Earth Volume 1 (Technical) by ICR

Radioisotopes and the Age of the Earth Volume 2 (Technical) by ICR

Thousands . . . Not Billions by Don DeYoung

www.answersingenesis.org/go/dating

www.answersingenesis.org/go/young

www.answersingenesis.org/go/anthropology

www.answersingenesis.org/go/history

www.answersingenesis.org/go/compromise

06

Now the flood was on the earth forty days. The waters increased and lifted up the ark, and it rose high above the earth. The waters prevailed and greatly increased on the earth, and the ark moved about on the surface of the waters. And the waters prevailed exceedingly on the earth, and all the high hills under the whole heaven were covered. The waters prevailed fifteen cubits upward, and the mountains were covered.

And all flesh died that moved on the earth: birds and cattle and beasts and every creeping thing that creeps on the earth, and every man. All in whose nostrils was the breath of the spirit of life, all that was on the dry land, died.

Genesis 7:17–22

What You Will Learn

The geologic column is a graphic representation of the layers of rock that make up the earth's crust. By compiling data from local areas, scientists have constructed a composite picture of the earth. Evolutionists would have us believe that this is also a picture of the 4.5 billion year history of the earth. Using a bit of circular reasoning, the geologic column is used as support for biologic evolution, which is then sometimes used to confirm the order of the layers in the geologic column. The use of radiometric dating is also applied to the layers of the geologic record to establish the *absolute* ages of the layers and the billions of years indicated by the rock layers. In order for life to have evolved, the earth must be extremely old, so the assumption of long ages is applied to the geologic record to support the evolutionary philosophy.

From the biblical creationist perspective, there are several events that must be considered when interpreting the evidence of the earth's history recorded in the rocks. Just as evolutionists assume that the earth began as a random, molten mass, biblical creationists assume that the earth began with supernatural acts of God—forming the original rocks and layers. These layers and rocks were then catastrophically rearranged and redeposited during the Genesis Flood. As the waters covered the earth, and later flowed off the continents as the mountains rose, the major erosional features, like Grand Canyon and Uluru, were carved out. Modern examples of canyon formation and rapid erosion provide models to explain how many formations can be described by the Flood and its after-effects—and all within a few thousand years.

The real difference comes down to interpreting the evidence based on man's understanding of billions of years, or using the Word of God as a starting point. There is no disputing the facts of the geologic record, but the facts don't speak for themselves. They must be interpreted!

What Your Textbook Says about the Geologic Column

Evolutionary Concept	Prentice Hall	Glencoe	Holt	Articles
The fossil and rock records provide clues to the past and the future.	—	132, 553, 569	—	6:2, 6:3
Index fossils are used to identify rock layers and correlate layers that are disconnected.	337, 341–343, 345–346, 356–357	T551, T552C, 557–561, 568, T609, 609, 629	187–188, 197, 200, 211–213, 222, 232–233	6:1, 6:2, 6:3
Geologists divide the earth's 4.6 billion year history into time periods represented by distinct rock layers.	T92C, 342, 352–353, T354, 354, 364–365, 377, 382, 386–387	T550, T552C, 553–556, T591, T615, 626, 628, 635, 648, T649, T687	66, 152, 185, 208, T210, 211, 213–214, 217, 226	4:1, 4:3, 5:1, 6:1, 6:3, 6:5, 7:11
Major rock formations (Devils Tower, Uluru, etc.) formed in the distant past and have been constantly eroding.	298	T51, 153, 428, 635–636, 662	T123C, 191, 349	6:3, 6:5, 6:6, 6:7
Sediments have been deposited over millions of years and are used to calculate ages.	T345, T407, 408	226, 229, 429, 612–613, 627	188, 192	4:1, 4:3, 5:1, 6:1, 6:2, 6:3, 6:4, 6:5, 6:7, 6:8, 7:11
Canyons form over millions of years.	—	T522D, 553, 557	186, 364, T381	6:5, 6:6
Mountains formed millions of years ago and are gradually eroded.	317, T372, 379	526–527, 531, 537	256, 272, T282, 363	6:7, 6:9
Folding and deformation of rocks occurs gradually.	80–82, 308–309, 338	—	—	6:5, 6:7, 6:9
Limestone caves form gradually.	177	T245, 245	—	6:10

Evolutionary Concept	Prentice Hall	Glencoe	Holt	Articles
Ripples can be preserved in rocks.	—	127	188	6:8, 7:7
Salt and other minerals formed as ancient seas evaporated.	T412	T195, T624D, 649	496	5:1, 6:11
Ancient reefs formed major rock formations.	—	613–614	—	6:12

Note: Page numbers preceded by "T" indicate items from the teacher notes found in the margins of the Teacher's Edition.

What We Really Know about the Geologic Column

Before we begin looking at the geologic column, it is important to understand the key differences between the starting assumptions of young-earth geologists and old-earth geologists. These two different beliefs are used to interpret the evidence found in the rock record. Understanding these starting points is the key to understanding the different views of geologic time.

Young-earth creationists start with the Bible to derive the age of the earth: approximately 4,000 years passed between Creation and the coming of Christ, which is added to the 2,000 years since the time of Christ. This gives an age of the earth and universe of 6,000 years. They accept that God created in six days, that the once "very good" creation has been marred by sin (Genesis 3), and that a global Flood inundated the earth about 4,300 years ago (God's judgment on the sin of mankind, Genesis 6–9). They then interpret the evidence in light of these truths revealed in the eyewitness testimony of the Bible. The events of Creation Week (Genesis 1) and the Genesis Flood (Genesis 6–9) are the major shapers of the geologic record from a biblical perspective.

From the uniformitarian perspective, the planet has evolved gradually from a molten ball to a water-covered planet where mountains are continuously eroded and uplifted, and rocks are recycled through the earth's crust and mantle over billions of years. The use of radiometric dating is used to establish absolute dates for the age of the earth. Uniformitarian geologists accept catastrophes on a local scale, but reject any notion of global events like the Genesis Flood. The Bible is rejected as authoritative, and the earth is calculated to be 4.5 billion years old.

The major problem with uniformitarianism, from a scientific perspective, is that it is an unverifiable assumption—the same claim leveled against creationists and the Bible (except that creationists have a written eyewitness account). There is no absolute way to measure rates at which past events happened. Uniformitarianism is a presupposition applied to geology and the rock record, and also to biology, astronomy, physical chemistry, and many other scientific fields.

Now that we understand those starting points, we can take a closer look at the geologic record. There is no place on earth where we can find every rock layer in a continuous sequence. The geologic column presented in textbooks is a composite of many smaller columns that can be identified from direct observation. However, the presence of a general order in the rock record is undeniable. Questions about the nature of the geologic column ultimately center on the origin of the rock record. Those who start with a biblical view see the layers as evidence supporting the Creation Week and the global Flood described in Genesis (Genesis 1–2 and 6–9 respectively). Those who reject the clear teaching of the Bible interpret the rock record as a 4.5 billion year history of the earth.

There are many misconceptions about the nature of the geologic record and the geologic column used to represent the rock record. It helps to understand how the standard geologic column was constructed.

The concept of mapping and explaining rock layers began with Nicolaus Steno, who published on the geology of Tuscany in 1669. Steno set forth the basic rules followed by geologists today when examining field evidence. He actually based his reasoning on the biblical account of the Flood and accepted that the earth was only about 6,000 years old—a Bible–believing creationist laid the foundation for modern geology!

His Law of Superposition states that upper layers were deposited after the lower layers. The Principle of Original Horizontality states that sedimentary layers are deposited in flat layers that may later be disturbed. The Principle of Cross-Cutting Relationships states that a fault or intrusion must be younger than the layers it affects. All of these ideas can be used by both uniformitarian and biblical geologists to identify the relative ages of sediments.

During that same period, other geologists and theologians used the account of the Flood to understand the layers of sediment and the fossils contained in them. The understanding of the day was based on the idea that a major catastrophe had shaped the globe.

Catastrophism: the doctrine that changes in the geologic record are a result of physical processes operating at rates that are dramatically higher than are observed today (note: although the biblical view is one of many catastrophist views, not all catastrophist views are biblical).

Contrary to the catastrophist view, James Hutton and Charles Lyell argued that the present is the key to the past. They viewed the layers of sediments as products of vast ages of time. The processes forming and eroding rocks today are the same as they have always been.

Geology was divided between catastrophists who believed many large-scale floods had shaped earth's rock record and uniformitarians who believed in gradual processes. Eventually, the ideas of Hutton and Lyell came to dominate geologic thinking, and the Bible was thrown out of geology despite the efforts of some geologists who remained faithful to Scripture. Sadly, many theologians also adopted old-earth ideas and reinterpreted Scripture to align with the thinking of man.

Uniformitarianism: the doctrine that present-day processes acting at similar rates as observed today account for the change evident in the geologic record.

William Smith first used the similarity of fossils to construct detailed geologic maps across wide areas. He used fossils to map and correlate rock layers and constructed the first geologic map of England and Wales in 1815. Smith was a creationist who believed in the old-earth view now known as progressive creationism. By the early 1800s the idea of an old earth was popular, though the idea of a global flood was still used to explain many geologic deposits.

The standard geologic column was constructed by combining descriptions of local areas to form a composite record. By 1885 the finer divisions of the column had been identified based on the principles established by Steno, Smith, and Lyell. These ideas were also beginning to impact the study of biology, and Lyell's long-age ideas played a major role in Darwin's development of the theory of biological evolution over vast geologic eras.

Index fossils played an important role in the development of the geologic column. The idea that life became increasingly complex over time, whether by some evolutionary force or continuous creation by God, was used to analyze the fossils in the rock layers. It was assumed that by identifying the order of fossil succession, the layers could be correlated from one region to the next. Index fossils are still one of the major indicators of the age of a given layer.

GEOLOGIC TIME SCALE

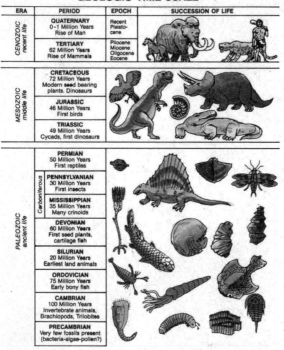

ERA	PERIOD	EPOCH	SUCCESSION OF LIFE
CENOZOIC recent life	QUATERNARY 0-1 Million Years Rise of Man	Recent Pleisto-cene	
	TERTIARY 62 Million Years Rise of Mammals	Pliocene Miocene Oligocene Eocene	
MESOZOIC middle life	CRETACEOUS 72 Million Years Modern seed bearing plants. Dinosaurs		
	JURASSIC 46 Million Years First birds		
	TRIASSIC 49 Million Years Cycads, first dinosaurs		
PALEOZOIC ancient life	PERMIAN 50 Million Years First reptiles		
	PENNSYLVANIAN 30 Million Years First insects	Carboniferous	
	MISSISSIPPIAN 35 Million Years Many crinoids		
	DEVONIAN 60 Million Years First seed plants, cartilage fish		
	SILURIAN 20 Million Years Earliest land animals		
	ORDOVICIAN 75 Million Years Early bony fish		
	CAMBRIAN 100 Million Years Invertebrate animals, Brachiopods, Trilobites		
	PRECAMBRIAN Very few fossils present (bacteria-algae-pollen?)		

Illustrations like this one are actually made by combining pieces of the geologic column from all over the world. Geologists make many assumptions when trying to explain all of the fossils and rock layers.

Shelled creatures such as ammonites and mollusks are the most commonly used index fossils.

Despite the confidence in index fossils, there is much criticism of their use—from both creationists and evolutionists. Slight differences in shell shape or structure are used to assign the shell to a new species, despite the variation apparent within a single living species today.

Another problem with index fossils is that, rather than being proof of evolution, evolution is already assumed to have occurred. The changes in features in index fossils of different periods are assumed to be caused by evolution, and the presence of different organisms in different periods is then used to support biological evolution. This is a case of using an assumption to prove the assumption is true—circular reasoning by any measure.

The geologic timescale we know today was not added to the column until after the development of radiometric dating techniques. Lyell and others had promoted the idea of millions of years of geologic history, but dates were not assigned to given layers until much later. Working on the assumptions of naturalism and uniformitarianism, the rock record was interpreted from these starting points. By the time radiometric dating techniques were implemented, the idea of millions of years of earth history had already become an established scientific "fact." Using uniformitarian assumptions (see the discussion in chapter 4), the radiometric dating techniques are put forward as support for the timescale of the standard geologic column.

As ideas on the formation and age of the earth changed, the ages assigned to the layers of the geologic column changed along with them. Different radiometric dating techniques have been developed to date the rocks, and thus the fossils in adjacent layers, but the use of index fossils is still the primary method of identifying and describing the strata in the rock record. If the ages determined for a fossil do not fit the presuppositions, the ages are often massaged until they *fit* within evolutionary thinking. Far from being independent from geological uniformitarianism, biological evolution is supported by the ages and the ages are supported by the fossils and their supposed evolution. The dating game played by

In the textbooks, the geologic record is correlated to the geologic periods that are alleged to extend over millions of years.

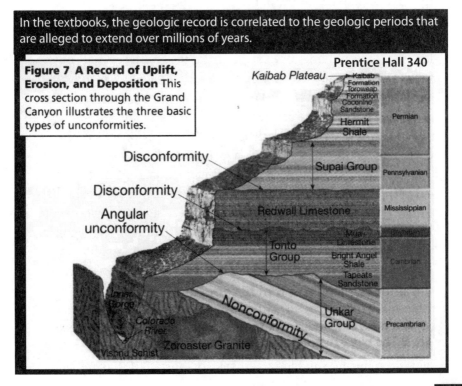

Figure 7 A Record of Uplift, Erosion, and Deposition This cross section through the Grand Canyon illustrates the three basic types of unconformities.

Prentice Hall 340

anthropologists to make the fossils fit the expected dates is as unscientific and subjective as you could imagine. This will be discussed in more detail in chapter 7 and is also demonstrated in article 6:2.

Despite the slow and gradual ideology of modern geology, the evidence is clearly explained by the biblical model—specifically relating the majority of the fossil-bearing geologic record to the Genesis Flood. Although there is much discussion among creationists about the details relating the Flood and creation to the geologic column, all agree that the majority of the fossil-bearing rock record is a product of the Genesis Flood and that any model must first be aligned with Scripture. Details such as exactly where the pre-Flood/Flood/post-Flood boundaries lie in the geologic column are still being evaluated. Nevertheless, the evidence of a global flood and rapid processes is overwhelming.

The layers exposed in the walls of Grand Canyon and in the Colorado Plateau region provide evidence of a catastrophe that must have covered at least the entire North American continent. The layer known as the Navajo Sandstone contains minerals that were eroded from the Appalachian Mountains. A river is used to explain this in the uniformitarian model, but a global Flood makes more sense of the evidence. The Tapeats Sandstone contains large boulders and was deposited in storm conditions over an immense area of north America. The Redwall Limestone extends from the Southwest to Pennsylvania and Tennessee—obviously deposited as the result of a massive catastrophe. Slow and gradual processes cannot explain these features of the rock record. (See article 6:7 for more examples.)

Layers that are all similarly bent are strong evidence in support of the rapid deposition of the layers exposed in Grand Canyon. Though there is an alleged time difference of 300 million years between the deposition of the Tapeats Sandstone and of the Kaibab Limestone, the layers have been bent to a similar angle by the Kaibab Upwarp (which allegedly occurred 70 million years ago). In places, the layers of the Tapeats Sandstone are bent at a 90° angle. These formations indicate that the layers must have been soft when the folding occurred. Had they been solid rock they would have fractured, but there is no evidence of fracturing. Heat and pressure can also cause deformation of rocks, but there is no evidence of that in the minerals and structure of these rocks. If the layers were deposited during the Flood and folded shortly after, there would not have been time for the rocks to harden and fracture.

As we look at the processes forming and eroding geologic structures today, we must admit they cannot be responsible for the features that we see across the globe. Textbooks and other evolution-based sources suggest Grand Canyon formed gradually over the last 6–17 million years, slicing through layers that go back nearly 2 billion years. This amazing canyon has been interpreted as the result of a little water acting over a very long period of time. However, from the biblical perspective, the canyon formed from a lot of water acting over a short period of time.

Grand Canyon itself is best explained as a result of the erosion caused by the sudden release of water from large lakes left behind after the Flood. The Flood deposited many of the canyon's layers, through which the canyon was later cut. Hopi and Canyonlands Lakes were remnants of the receding Floodwaters, impounded by the Kaibab Upwarp. While the sediment layers of the Kaibab Upwarp were still relatively soft, these lakes breached that barrier and their waters flowed west toward the Pacific Ocean, scouring the landscape. Could such a catastrophe actually carve such dramatic features? Evidence from the recent eruptions at Mount Saint Helens lends support to these claims.

After the eruption of Mount St. Helens in 1980, pumice and volcanic ash deposits blocked the Toutle River. Two years later a mud flow breached the area and eroded what is now known as the "Little Grand Canyon of the Toutle River," cutting canyons up to 140 feet deep. The side canyons and channels resemble the appearance of Grand Canyon and mirror the rapid formation of a canyon in a short period. Nearby, Loowit Canyon was cut out of solid rock to a depth of 100 feet. These observed examples of rapid canyon formation can be used to help us understand how larger canyons and topographic features may have formed as a result of the Flood.

Another striking example is the flood of ancient Lake Missoula. This Ice Age lake in Montana and Idaho experienced a catastrophic natural dam failure that resulted in the formation of the Channeled Scablands of Washington, including the Palouse Canyon. These areas were eroded rapidly, resulting in features that could not be explained by uniformitarian principles. Even uniformitarian geologists have come to accept the massive scale of the rapid formation of these areas. Again, these formations support the biblical model of a global Flood, and its aftereffects, with the power to form massive erosional features.

Two other major considerations of the geologic record are the catastrophic movement of the continents during the Flood and the Ice Age that resulted from the Flood. These two important aspects will be discussed in more detail in following chapters. Altogether, the evidence can be interpreted within the scientific model that includes the Creation Week and the Flood. The billions of years are not necessary to explain the geologic column. Six thousand years is enough time despite the uniformitarian claims to the contrary.

Ultimately, the fossil-bearing geologic record represents the wrath of God poured out in judgment on a world filled with sin. As we look at thistles and thorn bushes growing along a canyon where the layers of fossil-bearing sediment are exposed, how can we help but be reminded of God's justice? The rock record is a testimony to God's sovereign control over this earth from Creation to the Flood to today. The Ark is a testimony to His mercy which was ultimately demonstrated through the life, death, and resurrection of Jesus Christ.

Reference Article Summaries

6:1 Geological conflict, Snelling, www.answersingenesis.org/creation/v22/i2/geology.asp

The discovery of fossil wood in limestone with Jurassic period index fossils has provided the opportunity to date the rock with carbon-14 dating. This limestone layer would normally be given a date based on its position and index fossils. The Marlstone bed is estimated to be 189 million years old based on the ammonite and belemnite fossils. If the wood is truly that old there should be no traces of carbon-14 remaining.

Samples of the wood were sent to two testing facilities. Using accelerator mass spectrometry, a technique that can detect minute quantities of carbon-14, the labs found detectable carbon-14 in all of the samples. The age of the wood was calculated to be between 20,700 and 28,820 years old. The wood is obviously younger than the 189-million-year-old layer it was found in.

Knowing the wood could not contain radiocarbon after 189 million years, evolutionary geologists would never have tested it. They believe that limestone was formed slowly at the bottom of shallow seas where wood should not be found. A far more likely explanation is that the fossil marine animals and wood were buried during the global Genesis Flood. The carbon-14 dates are not inconsistent with the 4,500-year age when considering the different environment these organisms lived in prior to the Flood. In the evolutionary model, such inconsistencies cast doubt on the index fossil dating method and its uniformitarian and evolutionary assumptions.

6:2 The pigs took it all, Lubenow, www.answersingenesis.org/creation/v17/i3/pigs.asp

It is a myth that radiometric dating confirms the geologic timescale and the evolution of humans. The stories told by famous scientists have convinced most people of the idea of an earth that is millions of years old. However, a famous fossil hominid and its surrounding sediment have been assigned many different dates over time.

Since most sedimentary rocks and their fossils cannot be dated by radiometric dating volcanic ash (tuff) layers are used. The KBS (Kay Behrensmeyer Site) Tuff has hominid fossils and artifacts above and below it, so a maximum and minimum age can be assigned to those fossils. Skull 1470 was found by Richard Leakey in Kenya. He assigned it an age of 2.9 million years old based on the *modern* structure of the skull and earlier radiometric dates.

When the KBS Tuff was first potassium-argon (K-Ar) dated at between 212 and 230 million years old, the dates were automatically rejected as bad dates. Why? Because the scientists already *knew* that the layer should be between 2 and 5 million years old based on the fossils and artifacts it was near. Later testing adjusted the date to 2.61 million years based on minerals in the rock samples. This fitted Leakey's skull nicely, but hardly demonstrates that the radiometric dating is an independent confirmation of the fossil age. Dates that are *bad* with respect to the expected evolutionary model are set aside, and *good* dates are based on the fossils present. If the fossils were never found in this area, the tuff layer would have been considered to be over 200 million years old—a significant difference.

Later work on pig and elephant fossils, as well as paleo-magnetism, in the same sediments seemed to confirm the dating. However, the 2.9-million-year date was not acceptable in terms of human evolution. More dating put the skull between 1.6 and 1.82 million years old—a date Leakey resisted. Then in 1981 the layer was dated again at 1.87–1.89 million years. Ultimately, this is circular reasoning where the dates are *good* when they confirm the evolutionary thinking that they are used to support, and *bad* when they don't.

Prior to this (1975), the comparison of pig evolution, based on scant evidence, was used to suggest that the 2.6-million-year dates were off by 800,000 years and needed to be adjusted. Ultimately, the objective radiometric dating techniques were placed in doubt by the subjective arrangement of hypothetical pig evolution.

The first myth exposed by this account is that unless the correct rock is chosen to arrive at the correct date, the procedure was flawed or contaminated in some way. This presents a self-deceptive circular argument. Second, when a fossil is found and the search for a date begins, the correct date can be found by choosing the correct date from the options available. The fossils determine the radiometric date that is accepted. In this case the pigs won over the elephants, K-Ar, and other dating techniques. The evolutionary presuppositions dominate the interpretations—the facts do not speak for themselves.

6:3 Ten misconceptions about the geologic column, www.icr.org/article/242/107/

This article presents ten misconceptions about the geologic column, discussing the composition of the column, its correlation to the age of the earth, and the dating of layers from fossils and other uniformitarian assumptions. Some selected examples are discussed here.

The geologic column was actually constructed based on empirical evidence from the rock record by men who would be called progressive creationists in today's terms. The geologic time periods and eras were added later by uniformitarian scientists.

The geologic record for any given area is not always consistent with the geologic column shown in textbooks. The layers are sometimes out of order or absent which can make identifying the layers difficult. Using index fossils to correlate rock layers across continents is not always reliable, but data from drilling, seismic activity, and surface features allow many layers to be correlated across continents.

Radiometric dating often gives discordant ages to rock layers, and the process of sedimentation does not require millions of years. Connected to this idea are the illustrations of the geologic ages with their built-in evolutionary bias. However, these are just representations of what these sedimentary environments may have looked like and do not necessarily support the supposed evolutionary story they are supposed to represent.

6:4 Focus: rocks forming in months, www.answersingenesis. org/creation/v17/i2/focus.asp

Stones measuring up to a foot across are forming in a Norfolk (UK) marsh in a process which is happening in a few months or years. Small (and not-so-small) black lumps of rock are forming, as bacteria thriving on rotting vegetation produce "an iron-rich form of limestone, which acts as a mineral cement, binding the sand and mud together." Geologists have dug up similar stones before, which "often contain beautifully formed fossils." These fossils show a lot of detail of the soft flesh, "as it had no time to rot before the rock formed around it." Geology professor Max Coleman is keen to study the marsh. The rock is "forming faster than anyone had ever believed possible, with one stone creating itself in just six months" (Eastern Daily Press, UK, October

Uniformitarian thinking says that most canyons form from a little water over a long period of time. Catastrophism explains canyon formation from a lot of water over a short time. Canyons near Mount St. Helens and the scablands of eastern Washington provide evidence of canyon formation in a matter of days.

GOD'S WORD IS TRUTH   MAN DECIDES TRUTH

5, 1994). Creationists have long pointed out that hardening of sediments into rock is mainly a matter of the right cementing substances being present and that it doesn't require millions of years.

6:5 Grand Canyon strata show geologic time is imaginary, Walker, www.answersingenesis.org/creation/v25/i1/grandcanyon. asp

Visitors to Grand Canyon hear the usual geological interpretation involving millions of years. Guests are told that the horizontal formation at the bottom, the Tapeats Sandstone, was deposited 550 million years ago, and the Kaibab Limestone that forms the rim is 250 million years old. It is difficult to imagine the immense time involved in this interpretation. Interestingly, Grand Canyon strata extend over 250 miles into the eastern part of Arizona. There, they are at least one mile lower in elevation. Supposedly, the uplift of Grand Canyon area occurred about 70 million years ago—hundreds of millions of years after the sediments were deposited.

One would expect that hundreds of millions of years would have been plenty of time for the sediment to cement into hard rock. Yet, the evidence indicates that the sediments were soft and unconsolidated when they bent. Instead of fracturing like the basement rock did, the entire layer thinned as it bent. The sand grains show no evidence that the material was brittle and rock-hard, because none of the grains is elongated. Neither has the mineral cementing the grains been broken and recrystallized. Instead, the evidence points to the whole 4,000-foot thickness of strata being still flexible when it was uplifted. In other words, the millions of years of geologic time are imaginary. This flexible deformation of Grand Canyon strata dramatically demonstrates the reality of the catastrophic global Flood of Noah's day.

6:6 A canyon in six days! Morris, www.answersingenesis.org/go/walla-canyon

Most people are taught that Grand Canyon formed as the Colorado River eroded the landscape over millions of years. The fact that the same results could be accomplished with a lot of water over a short time is generally not mentioned. Observations of canyon formation in modern times suggest that Grand Canyon may have formed much as did a small canyon near Walla Walla, Washington—a lot of water over a short time. During an unusually wet period, a small irrigation ditch was used to divert some excess water. As the water passed through the ditch, it became a gully, then a gulch, then a canyon, 1,500 feet long and 120 feet deep. This all happened in six days, not millions of years. The similar formation of the Toutle River canyon near Mount St. Helens offers another example that is analogous to what would have happened as the Floodwaters receded in the days of Noah.

6:7 Uluru and Kata Tjuta: a testimony to the Flood, Snelling, www.answersingenesis.org/creation/v20/i2/uluru.asp

Uluru (also known as Ayers Rock) rises above the central Australian desert as an outcrop of many layers of sandstone. These layers are tilted at 80–85° and are nearly 4 miles thick. Uluru is composed of arkose (sandstone), and the randomly sorted mineral grains have jagged edges.

Kata Tjuta is nearby and is part of a conglomerate formation that extends over 25 miles. These layers are tilted at 10–18° and are composed of rounded boulders, cobbles, and pebbles cemented together by a finer matrix. It would seem that these two formations share a common history.

Evolutionists claim that the material for these two features was deposited as alluvial fans about 550–600 million years ago when the area was covered by a shallow sea. Repeated events of folding and faulting shaped the landscape and lifted these layers to the surface over 100 million years. The area has been exposed for the last 300 million years, creating the erosional features we see today. This is an interesting story, but does the evidence support it?

One problem with the story is the presence of fresh feldspar crystals in the Uluru arkose. These should have weathered to form clay if they had truly been exposed for hundreds of millions of years. Another problem is with the jagged edges and random mixing of the mineral grains. If these layers were slowly deposited over 50 million years, the edges would have become rounded and the particles would have been sorted by size and density. Even evolutionary geologists admit that the large boulders in the layers of Kata Tjuta must have been deposited relatively quickly by a torrent of water.

All of this evidence is far more consistent with a global flood that ripped up and redeposited materials in a very short time frame. The force of the water required to move these many thousands of feet of sediment into place in a short time is best explained as a result of the Genesis Flood catastrophe and the geologic activity that would have been associated with it. Ultimately, the uniformitarian assumptions are not consistent with the evidence of catastrophic depositional processes.

6:8 How long did it take to deposit the geologic column?
Morris, www.icr.org/article/2478

Evolutionists argue that although some sedimentary layers may have been deposited relatively quickly, the deposition of the entire column required hundreds of millions of years. Creationists suggest that the bulk of the fossil–

bearing sedimentary rocks were deposited during the one–year period of Noah's Flood and its associated geologic events. The uppermost surface of each layer should allow us to determine which explanation fits the evidence.

Distinct ripple marks on the surface of many sandstone layers make it clear that these layers were quickly covered. If millions of years had passed between these layers, the ripple marks would be eroded. The absence of animal burrows and plant roots in these layers also suggests a rapid sequence. Polystrate fossils that cross many layers also require the successive layers to be deposited quickly. The limited amount of erosional features, called unconformities, on a global scale also points to the rapid deposition of the rock layers. All of this is what we would expect from the Flood described in the Bible.

6:9 Recent rapid uplift of today's mountains, Baumgardner, www.icr.org/article/98

There is disagreement between the field observations of mountain formation and the theoretical uniformitarian models that are supposed to describe the process. The field data show processes that occur much too rapidly to fit the present rates accepted under uniformitarian assumptions. Because of the specialization that happens in much of science, many in the earth science community do not know such a problem explaining the uplift of mountains exists.

The biblical record, however, provides a straightforward explanation. The catastrophic processes of the Flood and the reworking of the crust formed the mountains very rapidly. As the earth's crustal plates stopped moving near the end of the Flood, the areas of thickened crust were forced upward to reach equilibrium. In the uniformitarian model, this uplift occurred in the last 5 million years. In the biblical time frame, the uplift occurred over a few hundred years after the Flood.

The case seems compelling that the Flood was accompanied by major tectonic activity. The fact that the ocean floor is young, even by uniformitarian standards, suggests an extremely rapid replacement during the events of the Flood. Computer models support this claim and provide a model to explain the rapid spreading of the continents accompanied by rapid subduction. This subduction would produce mountains along these boundaries in rapid fashion. How this rapid formation could occur in the uniformitarian model poses a serious problem.

The planation surfaces that precede the mountain-building phase are another problem in the uniformitarian model. These flat surfaces can be explained by sheet erosion due to the waters of the Flood flowing rapidly off of the continents and into the ocean basins as the continental crust bobbed up on the mantle. All of these processes are best explained by a recent, global Flood.

6:10 Limestone caves: a result of Noah's Flood? Doolan, Mackay, Snelling, Hallby, www.answersingenesis.org/creation/v9/i4/caves.asp

The extensive system known as Carlsbad Caverns was discovered by Jim White in 1901 and is just one of hundreds of limestone caves found around the world. The evolutionists would suggest that the caves began forming around 60 million years ago. The rock was gradually eroded along cracks, and intersecting channels eventually formed the labyrinth of caverns and passages.

The belief that these limestone caves (known as karst formations) formed as acidic water dissolved the rocks is based on four lines of evidence. First, modern caves show an ongoing process of solution by the formation of stalactites and stalagmites. Second, the structures found in caves match those found in solution experiments. Third, the passages follow fractures and the level of the land as would be expected by the natural flow of water. Fourth, caves resembling limestone caves do not occur in non-limestone rocks that are less soluble. However, these processes do not require millions of years to form caves.

Studies on limestone caves in Kentucky have shown that a volume 59 meters long by one meter square can be dissolved in one year at the current rates. So, at the present rate, long ages are not required to create large caverns. This study and others make it clear that these large cave formations could have formed rapidly within the biblical time frame.

The thick layers of limestone show that they were catastrophically deposited. These layers of lime sediment would have contained water that would then be squeezed out as the weight of the overlying sediment layers built up the pressure on them. The water would pass through internal cracks while the sediment was hardening. As the floodwaters receded, the layers were uplifted and contorted by tectonic activity. The resulting forces and erosion of the sediments overlying the limestone would allow more water to escape and further open existing channels.

After the majority of the floodwaters had receded, there would still be lots of groundwater containing acids from decaying vegetation. This would mix with carbon dioxide and cause the rapid solution of the cave features. Finally, the groundwater would slowly drain out, leaving the caverns behind where the stalactites and stalagmites would then form. Thus, what is generally explained through processes over millions of years can be easily explained within the biblical time frame of a few thousand years, commencing with the global Flood.

6:11 Does salt come from evaporated seawater? Morris, www.icr.org/article/532

Evolutionists suggest that salt deposits (so-called evaporites) form as seas are filled and evaporated over long ages. This is not consistent with the many salt beds we find in the geologic record. Many of the salt beds are extremely thick and cover vast areas. It seems quite inconceivable that huge basins could repeatedly fill and evaporate in cycles over millions of years and remain in the same location. Modern salt lagoons fill in, erode, and migrate, so the same processes acting today could not produce huge salt beds.

Modern evaporites are impure, with many organisms living in them due to other mixed-in sediments. Large salt beds are absolutely pure. Since they contain no fossils and are extremely pure, they must not have formed from evaporating seas over vast ages. Many now think the salt was extruded as warm-to-hot supersaturated salt brines passed upward along faults and then rapidly cooled when they came in contact with the colder surface water, thus immediately releasing their salt load *en masse* to form pure salt deposits. Today we find these pure salt deposits and other important minerals in similar deposits that can only be explained by catastrophic processes—the processes that accompanied the Genesis Flood.

6:12 Not ancient reefs but catastrophic deposits, Walker, www.answersingenesis.org/creation/v25/i1/catastrophic.asp

The large limestone deposits in New Mexico and Texas are believed by evolutionists to be an ancient reef. The fossils found in the layer are used by evolutionists to support an old-earth interpretation. They claim that it takes many thousands of years for reefs to form, so these deposits could not have been deposited during the year-long Flood.

A closer look at the alleged "fossilized" reefs shows that they are made of sediments not bound together by fossils in original growth positions, and some do not have a solid rock foundation. Their cores also do not show the types of growth structures found in modern coral reefs, while their angles of deposition, as well as other evidences, point to rapid sediment and fossil deposition. On the other hand, if these were pre-Flood reefs somewhat different to modern reefs, they could have been washed into place during the Flood.

Questions to Consider

1. How was the geologic column we see in the textbooks developed? When was the timescale added?

2. If the geologic column represents an order in the layers of Grand Canyon and radiometric dating is accurate, then why do layers lower in the canyon give dates much younger than upper layers?

3. If there are supposedly hundreds of millions of years between the layers at the top and bottom of Grand Canyon, why were the layers all folded the same way simultaneously without breaking? Would the bending of those layers be better explained if the layers were still soft?

4. How were the extensive sedimentary layers formed on top of one another? Could a global flood explain the deposition of these layers?

5. How do uniformitarian geologists explain the lack of erosion between many layers in Grand Canyon if they were deposited millions of years apart?

6. Why is a global flood rejected as an explanation for the geologic features we see on the earth today?

7. Are the index fossils a reliable way to date rock layers over billions of years of history if scientists can't agree on the classification of living creatures today?

8. How can a tiny river explain the deep, wide erosion of features like Grand Canyon? Could a massive flood explain their formation?

Tools for Digging Deeper

Creation: Facts of Life by Gary Parker

Evolution Exposed: Biology by Roger Patterson

Footprints in the Ash by John Morris and Steve Austin

Grand Canyon: Monument to Catastrophe (Technical) by Steve Austin

The Missoula Flood Controversy (Technical) by Mike Oard

The New Answers Book by Ken Ham et al.

The New Answers Book 2 by Ken Ham et al.

Radioisotopes and the Age of the Earth Volume 1(Technical) by ICR

Radioisotopes and the Age of the Earth Volume 2 (Technical) by ICR

Thousands . . . Not Billions by Don DeYoung

www.answersingenesis.org/go/dating

www.answersingenesis.org/go/geology

07

THE FOSSIL RECORD

Everybody knows fossils are fickle; bones will sing any song you want to hear.

—J. Shreeve, "Argument over a Woman,"
Discover 11 no. 8 (1990): 58.

What You Will Learn

Just like any other piece of historical evidence, fossils don't speak for themselves. Evolutionists believe that the fossil record supports their theory of the slow and gradual evolution of life from amoebas to astronauts. Creation scientists reject this view and choose to accept the biblical version of the origin of life on earth. The fossil record is instead primarily a record of the destruction and death caused by the Genesis Flood. Extensive fossil graveyards and coal deposits are more consistent with a global catastrophe than with slow and steady processes over millions of years.

The formation of fossils demands that the organisms be buried quickly in an environment free of oxygen where nothing will disturb them. We find few places like this on earth today. Flood conditions are ideal for forming fossils, and the global Flood described in Genesis provides a starting point to examine the fossil record. Far from showing gradual changes of one organism transforming into another, the fossil record shows fully-formed organisms appearing suddenly and disappearing—just what we would expect if life were created and then later judged by the Flood. The Bible offers a framework to understand the fossil record.

What Your Textbook Says about the Fossil Record

Evolutionary Concept	Prentice Hall	Glencoe	Holt	Articles
Living fossils are nearly identical to those found in the fossil record.	—	585, 610, 615	T209C	7:1
Plant evolution is preserved in the fossil record.	—	566, 610	—	7:2, 7:3
The oldest fossils are 3.5 billion years old.	368	585, 591	—	4:1, 4:3, 7:4
Fossils provide information about past environments.	—	566, 568–569, 609	197	7:5, 7:11
Fossil fuels formed gradually as organisms were buried in swamps millions of years ago.	85, 95–97, T366, 375, 377, 410	131, 231, 446, T533, 555, T600D, 612–613, 616, T682C, 686, T687, 687–690, 707, 741	38, 159, 276	7:6, 7:7, 7:8, 7:11
Intact mammoth fossils have been found in arctic ice.	—	566, 572	—	7:9
Fossils provide information about how life on earth has evolved.	343, 383	566, 569	199	7:10, 7:11
Organisms must be buried quickly to be fossilized.	345	—	198	7:5, 7:9, 7:11

Note: Page numbers preceded by "T" indicate items from the teacher notes found in the margins of the Teacher's Edition.

What We Really Know about the Fossil Record

We should start the discussion about fossils by recognizing that the fossil evidence is shared by everyone. There are not creationist fossils and evolutionist fossils, but there are creationist and evolutionist interpretations of the fossils. When we observe fossils in the present, we can take measurements and determine composition, but the real interest in fossils is interpreting where they came from. Once we start attempting to explain how the organisms came to be fossilized or how and where they lived before they died, we must remember that we are using presuppositions in that explanation—we have gone from operational to historical science.

As mentioned in an earlier chapter, the fossil record does show a general order as we move from the lowermost geologic layers to the uppermost. Evolutionary geologists would interpret this order as the progression of life from simple chemicals to single cells to zebras and eventually to humans. The assumed progression in the fossil record is used to prove that biological evolution through natural selection changed one kind of organism into another over millions of years. There are many fossils that occur out of sequence that are explained away to confirm the presupposition of an old earth and biological evolution.

Creation scientists begin with the assumption that the fossil record can be primarily divided into two segments: the fossils deposited during the Flood and those formed since the floodwaters receded. Instead of assuming that the fossils represent vast ages during which life evolved, the Bible is used as the starting point. The Bible teaches that life was created as distinct kinds that have reproductive boundaries. Creation scientists reject the idea that the fossils demonstrate the evolution of life based on their belief in the Bible. Molecules-to-man evolution is based on naturalism and is contrary to the Bible.

Far from showing organisms changing, the fossil record is very static—organisms appear fully formed and then disappear or remain today. The lack of change recorded in the fossil record is used by some evolutionists to support the idea of punctuated equilibrium. This hypothesis suggests that evolution happened in rapid bursts over short periods. The lack of transitional forms and the sudden appearance of new organisms in sedimentary layers are used to support this idea.

Fossil: preserved remains of once-living organisms.

When creation scientists look at the fossil evidence they interpret it in light of the Flood described in Genesis. So how can the Flood model be used to explain the general order seen in the fossil record? The answer is that in general, the lower layers record the organisms that were buried first in the Flood, and the upper layers record the later stages of the Flood. The model that seems to best fit the evidence involves different ecological zones being buried at different times. Using the description of the Flood in Genesis and the fossil evidence, the stages of the Flood are recreated to explain the fossil record.

The presence of sea-dwelling creatures in layers lower than those containing dinosaurs does not mean that the dinosaurs lived after the sea creatures. To make this claim, it must be assumed that the layers were deposited over vast ages and that evolution is true. Since the Flood was a global event that lasted about one year—as Genesis clearly teaches—we would expect to find massive layers of sediment containing the fossilized remains of billions of animals and plants. And that is exactly what we find all around the globe. There certainly are questions that remain about the details of the model, but the foundational ideas explain much within the limits of historical interpretations.

Some of the greatest testimonies to a worldwide flood are the many, massive fossil graveyards across the globe. One of the most popular in the United States is Dinosaur National Monument near Vernal, Utah. "The Wall" is an exposed sandstone graveyard which contains the fossilized remains of stegosaurs, camarasaurs, diplodocuses, freshwater clams and snails, logs, and many other organisms. The National Park Service website (http://www.nps.gov/history/museum/exhibits/dino/douglas.html) explains the remains as the result of a dried up waterhole where many dinosaurs perished 150 million years ago. After the drought, the river filled again and slowly covered the carcasses with sand and gravel, and the fossilization process began.

That is a nice story, but that is not how fossils form, let alone a layer 50 feet thick. Organisms must be buried quickly in an environment that lacks oxygen in order to be fossilized. If they are not, scavengers and bacteria will quickly decompose the organisms. The most common fossils at the site are freshwater clams. Most of these clam shells are found opened, showing that they were buried after death. However, some of the clams are found still closed, indicating that they were buried while still alive. The clams could not have been buried alive if the river and waterhole had dried up. That explanation also fails to mention the large amounts of volcanic sediments at the site. The presence of large amounts of volcanic activity associated with the Flood, combined with mudflows, is a much better explanation for this fossil graveyard and many others around the world.

The presence of fossils from marine and terrestrial organisms in graveyards around the world cannot be explained by the slow processes seen today. The Green River Formation, a fossil-rich formation in Wyoming, includes birds, bats, fish, insects, and many plant species all buried together. The Redwall Limestone of Grand Canyon contains fossil nautiloids (squid-like creatures with a shell) and other marine creatures buried by a fast-moving slurry that involved 24 cubic miles of lime, sand, and silt. No river or lake today can account for the scale of these graveyards. This is another reason why many geologists today are reexamining the fossil record from a catastrophic

The presence of many millions of nautiloids killed and fossilized in the Redwall Limestone is best explained by a single catastrophic event. The large scale of this graveyard, and similar features around the world, are best explained by the global Flood described in Genesis.

perspective—though not necessarily the biblical catastrophe.

Contrary to popular belief, rocks and fossils actually form quite rapidly. The formation of fossils requires the conditions that we would normally associate with a flood. If a fish dies in a lake or river it is extremely unlikely that it will form a fossil. It will be quickly picked apart by scavengers and torn apart by currents. The exquisitely preserved fish fossils that we find across the globe can only be explained by rapid burial in an environment that would prohibit decomposition. We do not find these conditions in very many places on earth today, yet fossils are found across the globe throughout the geologic column.

Sedimentary rocks can form in short periods of time instead of requiring millions of years to form. Rocks have been observed to form over observable time periods, similar to the everyday process of making concrete from a mixture of lime, sand, and gravel. The organisms trapped in rapidly deposited layers are much more likely to become fossilized than those that are not buried in some sort of catastrophe. The ideal way to make a fossil of your pet fish would be to quickly add some concrete mix to the bowl.

Extensive coal beds and oil reservoirs are also examples of fossil graveyards. The textbooks explain coal beds as the remains of plants gathered in shallow seas and swamps over geologic time. Pictures of lush landscapes with foreign plants and giant insects are used to make the story more believable. One problem is that we do not see swamps forming coal today. Boggy areas today cannot explain the massive coal deposits seen in the geologic record. Features like compressed bark sheets, polystrate trees, and sharp boundaries do not match the descriptions of formation given by the textbooks. (See articles 7:7 and 7:8 below for more information.) The presence of carbon-14 in coal samples (as published by the RATE group) also demonstrates the recent formation of coal. The Flood can explain the rapid burial of enormous amounts of vegetation that became the coal we use today. Coal, as well as oil and natural gas, can be formed in hours in the laboratory—the millions of years are not required.

Other testimonies of rapid burial include the trackways of organisms such as horseshoe crabs, trilobites, various dinosaurs, pterosaurs, and amphibians. In order to be preserved, these tracks must have been covered very soon after they were made. Under

Vast swampy seas are alleged to have formed coal beds over millions of years. However, coal forms quite rapidly under the right conditions. These ancient swamps are not necessary to explain where our fossil fuels came from.

Figure 10 Model of a Pennsylvanian Coal Swamp Shown are scale trees (left), seed ferns (lower left), and scouring rushes (right). Note the large dragonfly.
Prentice Hall 375

the slow, gradual processes seen in today's lakes, rivers, and seas, the tracks would have been obliterated by burrowing organisms, waves, and currents. The footprints at Laetoli, Tanzania, are dated at 3.7 million years old. The prints are preserved in ash deposits from a nearby volcano that was damp from a passing rain. Before more rain could erase the tracks, another layer of ash was deposited, thus preserving the tracks. Among those of common animals are the footprints of what would seem to be modern humans, but modern humans didn't appear until much later according to the evolutionary view. Evolutionists won't admit these are modern footprints, but instead use them to suggest that our human ancestors have been around for about 4 million years. The details of alleged human evolution become more confusing as more evidence is made available and interpreted.

It is interesting that the textbooks do not mention polystrate fossils at all. The presence of fossils that penetrate many layers is a major problem for uniformitarian explanations. The cliffs at

Joggins, Nova Scotia, present a prime study of polystrate fossil trees. These fossilized trees pass through many of the layers of the exposed cliff face. If the layers represent many millions of years, how were the trees able to stand upright without rotting away while they were slowly buried? Some suggest that the trees were buried and fossilized while the surrounding layer was then weathered and the next forest grew on top of that layer, to be subsequently buried by the slow deposition of the next layer. Repeat the process over millions of years and it supposedly creates polystrate fossils. The fossil trees at Specimen Ridge in Yellowstone National Park are another example of this phenomenon.

The Flood, once again, offers a better explanation. After observing the events following the eruption of Mount St. Helens and the floating logs in Spirit Lake, Dr. Steve Austin provided another explanation. The tree stumps and logs floating on the lake eventually settled to the bottom as they became waterlogged. Many sank root end first with sediment and bark layers around and between them. Underwater photographs have revealed similarities to the petrified forests—successive layers of buried upright stumps with no roots. This model provides a Flood-based explanation and is supported by observational evidence.

The presence of living fossils is another quandary for those who interpret the fossil record from an evolutionary perspective. Thousands of organisms have remained virtually unchanged over alleged millions of years of earth's history. One of the most famous

The presence of "living fossils" like this coelacanth casts doubt on the value of evolution as a predictive model—organisms can change rapidly or stay the same for hundreds of millions of years. Other examples of living fossils include wasps, dragonflies, stromatolites, ginkgoes, clams, and the Wollemi pine.

accounts is that of the coelacanth. The coelacanth was believed to be extinct as none had been found in the fossil record in the last 65 million years of sediments. Then, in 1938, a living specimen was caught off of the coast of South Africa. Since then, another species in Indonesia has been found. How does something avoid being discovered in the fossil record over 65 million years?

Evolutionists suggest that a shallow-water species of this fish became extinct and no deep-water specimens have been subsequently lifted to the surface to be discovered. They believe there must be more fossils, but we just haven't found them yet. Creation scientists would suggest that the fossilized members were buried during the Flood, and that the other members have survived in the oceans undetected by scientists until recent times. The same would be true of the ginkgo tree, Wollemi pine, dawn cedar, sturgeon, crocodilians, frilled shark, and many insects, crinoids, crustaceans, and mollusks.

Accepting that these organisms have remained virtually unchanged for tens of millions of years exposes the plastic nature of evolutionary theory. In the same amount of time, other organisms have supposedly undergone major changes through the same evolutionary processes. Can evolution be falsified as a theory if it explains both no change and major change? Or is it a perfect theory because of its ability to absorb any evidence—regardless of how contradictory it may appear? We will explore that idea more in the next chapter.

The fossil record can be viewed either as the progression of life through random chance over 3.5 billion years, or as the remnants of a global Flood which happened about 4,300 years ago. Starting with the authority of Scripture, we can explain the evidence in the fossil record—from massive graveyards to living fossils—in a consistent manner. It is not necessary to throw the Bible out of discussions over fossil evidence. It is not necessary to try to fit evolutionary ideas into the Bible. All we need to do is begin with the eyewitness accounts found in the Bible, and we can explain the world around us.

Reference Article Summaries

7:1 "Living fossils" enigma, Catchpoole, www.answersingenesis.org/creation/v22/i2/living_fossil.asp

There are thousands of examples of creatures living today that are virtually identical to their ancestors which supposedly lived hundreds of millions of years ago. These include many insects, the Wollemi pine, ginkgo trees, crocodiles, coelacanths, and many marine invertebrates. How can evolution explain that some creatures have remained unchanged for such long periods of time while others have changed relatively rapidly? There is no real consistent answer. Some say it is due to long generation times, but that doesn't work for cockroaches and bacteria that reproduce in days or minutes. Some say that it is just chance and luck, but that is intellectually unsatisfying to many scientists. Others say it is because of the lack of habitat change, but that only works in a few examples. Ultimately, evolutionists can provide no clear explanation of why these "living fossils" are still with us today. Creationists, however, understand that the ancestors of these organisms were created only 6,000 years ago. This timeframe makes the explanation rather simple—they have survived relatively unchanged for a few thousand years, not millions.

7:2 Did plants evolve? Williams, www.answersingenesis.org/creation/v19/i4/plants.asp

The evolutionary sequence of plants is not displayed in the fossil record even though the story is told in textbooks. At least four different evolutionary lines are supposed to have emerged from prehistoric green algae, the common ancestor of all plants. In a recent text on plants, not a single fossil series is provided to support the phylogenetic tree diagrams that supposedly explain the evolutionary history of plants. The grand claims are laced with words like "probably," "apparently," and "presumably." The places where the fossil record is the most complete should provide the clearest picture of evolution, but this is where many evolutionists

Plants like these ginkgoes are virtually identical to those that appear suddenly in the fossil record.

disagree. The lack of fossil ancestors for the major groups would seem to be important, but the evolutionists fill in the gaps with imagination, not science. The evidence clearly points to diverse groups created in the supernatural events described in the opening chapter of Genesis.

7:3 Kingdom of the plants: defying evolution, Williams,
www.answersingenesis.org/creation/v24/i1/plants.asp

The evolution of plants offers unique challenges to evolutionary scientists. The simplest of plants is said to have evolved at different times from some type of chlorophyte algae, but this simple plant did not give rise to the more complex vascular plants. As one moves up the evolutionary ladder, there are no known ancestors for the majority of the major phyla of plants, and the chemical relationships do not support the common evolutionary models. Major changes to the organization of the phylogenetic tree of plant evolution have been suggested, but the order of events is still being debated. In many cases, the claimed ancestors appear later in the fossil record.

The major groups of plants appear suddenly and fully formed—the transitional species are not present in the fossil record. To explain the amazing complexity of the "most evolved" plants—those with flowers (angiosperms)—evolutionary forces have allegedly modified leaves into petals, sepals, anthers, ovaries, and other flower structures over vast ages. This claim is made even though there is no fossil evidence for the changes that occurred, and flowering plants appear fully developed in the fossil record. All of this evidence points back to the creation model and the fact that plants are observed, in the present and in the fossils, reproducing within preprogrammed limits and "after their kind."

7:4 Ancient organisms stay the same, www.answersingenesis.org/creation/v21/i3/news.asp

A while ago, evolutionists would not have expected to find any fossils in rocks that they thought were, say, three billion years old; life supposedly hadn't evolved yet. However, fossils of bacteria kept turning up in progressively older rocks (no surprise to creationists), which allowed less and less time for the first life to evolve in the hypothetical, oxygen-free early atmosphere. Now an Austrian/Swiss team of scientists has looked at rock from Western Australia's Pilbara region, supposedly around 3.5 billion years old, and found what appear to be fossilized cyanobacteria. These appear to be indistinguishable from the same (oxygen-producing) creatures making the mat structures called stromatolites in the shallows of Shark Bay, some 500 kilometers away on the coast.

7:5 High and dry sea creatures, Snelling, www.answersingenesis.org/articles/am/v3/n1/high-dry-sea-creatures

Many rock layers that are thousands of feet above sea level contain fossils of marine organisms. Even atop the Himalayas, fossil ammonites can be found in the limestone. So how do we explain this? At some point, the ocean waters must have covered the continents. The continents could not have been below sea level because the less dense continental rock "floats" on the mantle well above the ocean rocks. So the evolutionary explanations fail.

There are two mechanisms that explain how the water covered the continents. During the biblical Flood, the fountains of the great deep would have added water to the oceans for 150 days. Second, if the ocean floor rose it would have pushed the sea level up and caused the water to flood across the continents. The breakup of the earth's crust and less dense, heated molten rock of the newly forming seafloor could create this situation. As the new ocean floor rock cooled toward the end of the Flood, and the ocean basins sank as the mountains rose up, so the floodwaters would have returned to the ocean basins, leaving the fossils buried in the sediments deposited on the continents.

The Flood provides a model to explain how marine organisms were transported onto the continents and deposited. Later, as the mountains rose, these sediments were elevated high above sea level. Looking to the Bible, we can explain the world around us in a consistent way.

7:6 The origin of oil, Snelling, www.answersingenesis.org/articles/am/v2/n1/origin-of-oil

Oil is generally found in sedimentary rocks trapped in reservoirs created by faults or folding. Most scientists agree that the oil we find came from plants (and perhaps some animals) that were buried and chemically converted to crude oil and natural gas. The presence of porphyrins, chemicals similar to chlorophyll and hemoglobin, is important in understanding the formation of oil. Porphyrins break down rapidly in the presence of heat or oxygen. So, the plants that formed the oil must have been deposited in an environment free of oxygen.

These conditions do not match what we see happening today in river deltas and coastal areas, but can be found in places like the Black Sea. Rather than a gradual accumulation, the evidence seems to fit the rapid burial of tons of vegetation in an oxygen free environment.

Oils and the porphyrins they contain have been shown to be produced within hours and by no means require millions of years to form. Commercial thermal converters routinely turn animal slaughterhouse wastes into high-quality oil and fertilizer in two hours.

All of the available evidence points to a recent, catastrophic origin of oil from organic matter. The biblical Flood can explain the rapid deposition of massive quantities of vegetation under the conditions necessary to form the oil we harness today.

7:7 The polystrate trees and coal seams of Joggins Fossil Cliffs, www.icr.org/article/445

The cliffs at Joggins, Nova Scotia, preserve a unique geologic record that was used by Charles Lyell to convince the world that his uniformitarian ideas were correct. Lyell argued that the upright fossil trees could not have been deposited by a catastrophic flood. Standard thinking today suggests that the area was once a coastal basin or river flood plain that was periodically covered by sediment over a 10-million-year period.

Coal seams in the layers are thought to record successive swamps, 85 or more, that formed in the exact location in the sinking basin. The presence of fossil trackways, ripple marks, raindrop pits, and cross bedding make it clear that these layers were deposited in quick succession. If they were the remains of many years of gradual deposition all of these features would have been obliterated by burrowing animals.

Fossil trees that pass through many geologic layers representing millions of years are not well explained by slow and gradual processes. The Flood offers a better explanation.

The fossils in the layers include terrestrial and marine animals and plants, but the large trees are the most significant fossils. These tree trunks actually rise vertically through many different layers and are known as polystrate fossils. These trunks are separated from their roots and filled with different sediments and even fossil amphibians. Uniformitarian geologists claim that these trees grew in swamps and were slowly covered by muddy sediment as the swamps were flooded. New trees would then grow, so a new peat layer would form and the cycle would repeat.

It is highly unlikely that the above story is true. The presence of roots inside the trunks and scattered through the surrounding soil, as well as the absence of roots penetrating lower layers, discredit the idea that the trees grew in place. Well-preserved leaf fossils would not be present in the swampy conditions, and some of the trees are at an angle or upside down. The sandstones are cross bedded and many of the root fragments are oriented in a similar direction, indicating fast moving water.

All of these evidences are better explained as the result of a catastrophic Flood. Though all of the details are not fully worked out, the Flood model offers a much more coherent explanation of the evidence found at this location and many others.

7:8 Did modern coal seams form in a peat swamp? Morris, www.icr.org/article/521

Most geologists are trained to think that the present is the key to the past and thus consider coal to be a product of peat swamps from the distant past. Peat swamps of today are very small compared to the massive coal seams that cover entire states. The organic material that collects has the consistency of coffee grounds, unlike the sheets of bark and woody material that are found along with the fine grains in coal seams.

Ancient coal seams have knife-edge borders with the layers above and below them and rarely have roots penetrating those layers, as seen in peat swamps today. The adjacent layers are often classified as marine environments, which would have required the repeated downwarping and uplifting of an area. The lack of erosional features between coal and adjacent layers does not fit the story. The features of modern peat swamps cannot explain the features seen in coal seams, but the burial of massive quantities of plant material in alternating marine layers is better explained by a model that incorporates the Flood of the Bible.

7:9 Frozen mammoth carcasses in Siberia, Oard, www. answersingenesis.org/home/area/fit/chapter1.asp

The presence of frozen mammoth carcasses in the arctic permafrost has been a puzzle for centuries. Scientists struggle to explain why these large animals lived in Siberia—a land of blizzards and permafrost. Accompanying the mammoths are bison, horse, antelope, woolly rhinoceros, and other large mammals.

The amazing thing about the mammoths is that many of them appear to have been frozen in place while standing or sitting. This preservation happened so quickly that their last meal was preserved in their mouths and stomachs. Buttercups and grasses have been found indicating a much different environment at the time the mammoths inhabited Siberia. Exactly how the mammoths inhabited this area is difficult to explain in uniformitarian terms, but it can be explained by the Ice Age that followed the Flood of Genesis.

It is likely that there are many millions of fossilized mammoths in the Siberian permafrost and many more in Europe and North America.

From observing several of the intact mammoth and rhinoceros fossils, we conclude that they must have died of suffocation. This can be explained in light of huge dust storms during the Ice Age, but this explanation is rejected by uniformitarian scientists. Secular scientists have no realistic way to explain how such a large number of mammoths died in such a short period, let alone how they were buried in the permafrost. The model built on the biblical Flood and subsequent Ice Age explains these circumstances quite well.

7:10 Fossils—do they get more complex? www.answersingenesis.org/creation/v20/i2/fossils.asp

Evolutionary theory would predict that organisms lower in the geologic strata would be less complex than those in higher layers. When evolutionists looked at ammonite shells and descendant-ancestor pairs of vertebrates, no trend in increasing complexity was found.

7:11 How fast? Parker, www.answersingenesis.org/cec/docs/cfl-pdfs.asp

How fast do fossils and rock layers form? Just about everybody agrees that individual fossils must have formed quickly. When an organism dies, it must be buried quickly and deeply. Fallen trees in a forest, fish killed in red tides, and the bison that once roamed the plains of North America will not be fossilized. It is generally accepted that flood conditions are perfect for forming fossils. Creation scientists believe it was one Flood, and evolutionists believe it was many small floods that created the fossil record.

One of the most common ways fossilization occurs is when the pores of a bone or piece of wood are filled with mineral-rich water that forms crystals. Fossilization must have been rapid in the case of a miner's hat that fell into limey water and hardened to stone. Fossils can be made in the laboratory in a short time.

Fossilized jellyfish must have been fossilized very rapidly, because jellyfish washed up on the shore today disintegrate in a matter of hours. The formation containing these Ediacaran fossils covers a large area and includes millions of specimens of jellyfish and other organisms. These all must have been buried in a short period in wet, sandy conditions to preserve them.

Most people are taught that sedimentary rock takes millions of years to form, but we all know better—concrete can form solid rock in hours. Time, heat, and pressure can and do alter the properties of rock but are not necessary to form it. However, we don't find individual fossils or rock layers, but billions of fossils buried in many rock layers that form the geologic record.

Evolutionists suggest that the fossils in the geologic record show a progression of life from the bottom to the top. They claim that the "fact of evolution" is present in the rock record in the evolutionary story. Creation scientists view the rock record as a testimony to the global Flood described in Genesis. The differing life forms in the rock units represent ecological zones that were buried in succession during the Flood. Bottom–dwelling marine creatures were buried first, and then other sea creatures followed by the different ecological zones on the land.

Many evolutionists are adopting views of neo-catastrophism to explain the massive fossil-bearing layers covering large sections of continents and supposedly containing large gaps in time (known as paraconformities). The presence of polystrate fossils allegedly penetrating many millions of years of geologic layers is also best explained by rapid deposition of many layers, rather than a gradual process. The events following the eruption of Mount St. Helens have provided an explanation for the formation of polystrate trees in fossil forests and layers of bark that will eventually form coal deposits.

Questions to Consider

1. How fast can fossils form?

2. What conditions are necessary to form fossils?

3. How soon after death would a large dinosaur (or a group of large dinosaurs) need to be buried by sediment to prevent scavengers from scattering its bones? It would seem this would need to be a catastrophic event to bury this large animal in sediment.

4. How can polystrate fossils be explained if the layers they are buried in represent millions of years? Wouldn't the wood rot away before it was covered?

5. Don't large fossil graveyards suggest a major catastrophe? Could a massive flood explain these deposits?

6. How are massive fossil graveyards explained without a major catastrophe?

7. Where would we find fossils forming on earth today?

Tools for Digging Deeper

Creation: Facts of Life by Gary Parker

Evolution: The Fossils Still Say No! by Duane Gish

Evolution Exposed: Biology by Roger Patterson

Footprints in the Ash by John Morris and Steve Austin

Grand Canyon: Monument to Catastrophe (Technical) by Steve Austin

The New Answers Book by Ken Ham et al.

The New Answers Book 2 by Ken Ham et al.

Thousands . . . Not Billions by Don DeYoung

War of the Worldviews by Ken Ham et al.

www.answersingenesis.org/go/fossils

www.answersingenesis.org/go/living-fossils

www.answersingenesis.org/go/flood

08

The absence of fossil evidence for intermediary stages between major transitions in organic design, indeed our inability, even in our imagination, to construct functional intermediates in many cases, has been a persistent and nagging problem for gradualistic accounts of evolution.

—Stephen J. Gould, in *Evolution Now: A Century After Darwin*, ed. John Maynard Smith (New York: Macmillan, 1982), p. 140.

What You Will Learn

The evolution of life on earth from simple matter is accepted as a fact by secular science. Natural selection is claimed by evolutionists to support the belief that all life has emerged from a common ancestor over billions of years. Observational science has demonstrated that natural selection acts to decrease or conserve the amount of genetic information in a population. In order to turn an amoeba into an ape, there has to be an increase in genetic information. Despite this fact, evolutionists insist on the increasing complexity of life over time. To add to the problems of the evolutionary story, life must have evolved from nonliving chemicals. No one understands how this could have happened, but it is accepted as true regardless of any evidence.

The Bible presents a very different picture. God created all living things according to their kind in a series of supernatural acts. All life came from these original kinds, not from a single ancestor. The change that is evident in the fossil record is the result of change by natural selection within the created kinds. Dogs have become different types of dogs, but have never produced anything other than dogs. Man is not the result of an evolutionary process, but was created in the image of God as described in the Bible. The fossil record is not the result of gradual change over billions of years, but the record of the global Flood and events following it. Evolutionists look to outer space to find life on distant planets and attempt to communicate with beings beyond the earth when God, the "Ultimate Being," has already communicated to us through His Word.

What Your Textbook Says about
Biological Evolution

Evolutionary Concept	Prentice Hall	Glencoe	Holt	Articles
Evolution is a process of change over time and is accomplished by natural selection.	T362C, T374	T234, 566, 569	215, T237D, T257	8:1, 8:2, 8:3, 8:4, 8:5
Life evolved in the oceans first, along with oxygen in the atmosphere as a result of photosynthesis of primitive plants.	T92D, T362C–D, T367, 367, T420C–D, 477, 494, T642C	9, T270C, T389, 554–555 T576C, 578, 584, 585–591, T588, T590, 649	8, T209C, 216, 219, T373C, T469D	3:7, 8:1, 8:2, 8:4, 8:5, 8:6
Unicellular life evolved on earth first, followed by multicellular life over periods of millions of years.	368–369, T420D	T576D, 577, T591, 592–593, T608, 649	183D, T209C, 216–217	3:7, 8:2, 8:4, 8:5, 8:6
The Cambrian Explosion documents the sudden appearance of many life forms.	T362D, 371	T600C–D, 604, 649	218	8:2, 8:3, 8:7
Vertebrates diversified in the oceans, and reptiles evolved from amphibians mainly due to the evolution of the amniotic egg. This line eventually evolved into mammals and birds.	371, T374, 374–375, 380–381, T420D	555, T600D, T613, 615–616, T617, 628–629, 631, 650	214–215, 219–220	8:2, 8:8, 8:10, 8:11, 8:12, 8:13

Evolutionary Concept	Prentice Hall	Glencoe	Holt	Articles
Dinosaurs lived during the Mesozoic Period and went extinct 65 million years ago, but the theropods evolved into birds.	T356, 377, 380, T586C	22, 555, T632, 631–633, 644, 649–650, T892–897, 892–897	15, 199, T209C–D, 210, 221–222, T222,	8:2, 8:9, 8:12, 8:13
Mammals evolved alongside, and then replaced, dinosaurs.	383–384, T474D	222, 555, 628, 630, 639–640, 650	224	8:2, 8:10
Plants originated in the ocean and moved onto dry land over a period of millions of years.	374, 379, T383, 383	555, 609, 610, 629, 639, 650	—	7:2, 7:3, 8:2
Humans originated in Africa several million years ago and, although the fossil record is scarce, it indicates that humans didn't evolve from Neanderthals.	T315, 387, T420C, T424, T586C–D, T672C–D	555, T624D, 640–641, 650, T662	224	8:14, 8:15, 8:16
Many major extinction events have occurred in earth's history. Some were caused by meteorite collisions.	T1C, T92D, 375–376, T380, 381, T385, 385	555–565, T609, 616–617, 620, 628, 633–634, 650	221, 223, T740	8:9, 8:17, 8:18
Scientists are looking for life on other planets and in other places in the universe.	T420D, T642C–D, 650–651, 653, T656, T663	T9, T389, 577, T596, 596	T660, 703, 708, 735, T785, 785	3:7, 8:1, 8:4, 8:19, 8:20

Note: Page numbers preceded by "T" indicate items from the teacher notes found in the margins of the Teacher's Edition.

What We Really Know about Biological Evolution

Among Christians, there is a wide variety of views on biological evolution. Many accept the naturalistic explanations of the universe forming from a big bang and the earth evolving from gas and dust in space, but they reject the evolution of living things on earth. Why accept naturalistic explanations—even though they conflict with the Bible—and then reject the same reasoning when it comes to living things? Others accept the naturalistic explanation for biological evolution but insist that God guided the process or filled in the gaps. Why would God have used the death of billions of animals to bring about the pinnacle of His creation—mankind—when He is capable of creating everything in an instant? Is that the type of God who revealed Himself in the Bible? Questions like these are not often considered by those Christians who accept that secular science has provided the answers to many of life's questions. If we start from the Bible, we arrive at totally different conclusions.

A plain reading of Scripture reveals that God created all living things in the span of three days. Not only that, but Genesis 1:29–30 tell us that all creatures were created as vegetarians. There was no death in God's "very good" creation. It was not until

The story of evolution teaches that man is a product of death and suffering over billions of years (above). The Bible teaches that sin and death are products of mankind's rebellion against God (below)—quite opposite doctrines.

after sin entered the world that death entered in as a consequence. Today, we live in a world that is marred by sin and we must keep that in mind as we interpret the evidence. The Garden of Eden was not planted by God on top of sedimentary layers filled with death, thorns, and disease (all found in the fossil record). God created a perfect world that had not yet been marred by sin. Mankind and the rest of creation is awaiting the day when they will be freed from that corruption (Romans 8:20–22).

The topic of biological evolution is a very broad topic that cannot be covered in detail in this chapter. The companion to this book, *Evolution Exposed: Biology*, covers these topics in a more thorough manner. Please refer to that book for an in-depth discussion on biological evolution.

In order for us to begin the discussion of how amoebas are supposed to have evolved into apes, there is a more important question to ask. How did the first living thing come to be? Because modern science absolutely rejects the possibility of any supernatural influence, all life on earth must have come from nonliving matter. The story presented in the textbooks is that life evolved about 3.5 billion years ago from simple chemical interactions on the cooling earth. Experiments like those performed by Stanley Miller and Harold Urey are used to explain how life evolved from a primordial soup. These experiments are hailed as proof that life, somehow, appeared. There

WHAT IS THE CHANCE THAT THERE IS NO CHANCE
IN THIS DEMONSTRATION TO BEGIN WITH?!?!!

is little mention of the impossibility of such a transformation based on observational science. Instead, life is assumed to have appeared on a planet that is assumed to have formed from a collapsing nebula that is assumed to have formed from the big bang which is assumed to have occurred without a cause. If any of these links in the chain of assumptions breaks, the whole story of naturalism unravels.

The term evolution is used quite loosely in most circles—including the textbooks. In order to have an intelligent conversation, it is important to define the terms. Evolution, in biological terms, refers to the idea that all organisms are related to one another through time. The tree of life started with a single organism that changed over time to produce every form of life that has existed on earth.

Evolution: all life on earth has come about through descent with modification from a single common ancestor (a hypothetical, primitive, single-celled organism).

Evolution is generally assumed to happen as a consequence of natural selection. However, no direct observational evidence supports the concept of a fish turning, however gradually, into an amphibian. Natural selection is often used interchangeably with evolution but can better be defined as:

Natural Selection: the process by which individuals possessing a set of traits that confer a survival advantage in a given environment tend to leave more offspring on average that survive to reproduce in the next generation.

Natural selection is an observable process that falls into the category of operational science. We have observed mosquitoes, birds, and many microorganisms undergoing change in relatively short periods of time. New species have been observed to arise. Biblical creationists agree with evolutionists on most of the ideas associated with natural selection, except the idea that natural selection leads to molecules-to-man evolution. Evolutionary biologists assume, based on geologic interpretations, that there have been billions of years for this process to occur. But if long ages did not exist, the evolutionary theory cannot be true.

Another requirement for molecules-to-man evolution, a mech-

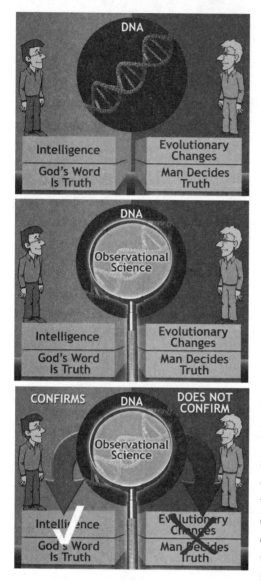

anism for adding new information, is also assumed to exist—even though it has never been observed. Natural selection deletes genetic information from the population. If natural selection is the mechanism that explains the successive adaptations in the transformation of a fish to an amphibian, it must provide new genetic information. To produce the new bones, muscles, and tendons in the limbs requires an elaborate orchestration of biologic processes. The bones don't only have to be present; they must develop at the right time in the embryo, have their shape and size predetermined by the DNA sequence, be attached to the correct tendons, ligaments, and blood vessels, attach to the bones of the pectoral girdle, and so on. The amount of information required for this seemingly simple transformation cannot be provided by a process that generally deletes information from the genome.

Biblical creationists consider major structures to be part of the original design provided by God. Modifications to those structures (adaptations) occur due to genetic recombination, random mutations, and natural selection. These structures do not arise from the modification of similar structures of another kind of animal. The beak of the woodpecker, for example, did not arise from the beak of a theropod dinosaur ancestor; it was an originally designed structure. The difference in beak shapes among woodpeckers fits with the idea of natural selection leading to changes within a population of woodpeckers—within the created kind.

Created Kind (Baramin): the original organisms (and their descendants) created supernaturally by God as described in Genesis 1; these organisms reproduce only their own kind within the limits of preprogrammed information, but with great variation.

Note: Since the original creation, organisms of one kind presumably cannot interbreed with a different kind, but individuals within a kind may have lost the ability (information) to interbreed due to the effects of the Curse.

This concept distinguishes biblically-based thinking from evolutionary thinking. Evolutionists would suggest that the first single-celled organism evolved into different multi-celled organisms. Eventually, a fish evolved from one of these lines (supposedly a relative of the starfishes) and then the fish evolved into an amphibian. The amphibians gradually developed features that allowed them to move away from water and eventually became reptiles which then evolved into birds and mammals. Eventually, the primates evolved and from that group the first humans emerged between 2 million and 200,000 years ago (depending on which source you put your faith in). The fossil record, DNA, and other biological molecules are used to support this idea.

When we look at what the Bible describes in Genesis, the idea of evolution from one kind of organism to another does not exist. The Bible describes organisms that were created after their own kind. The biblical kinds correspond roughly to the family level using today's classification scheme. Natural selection occurs within the kinds but could never produce a new kind of organism.

One of the most problematic spots in the explanation of the evolution of life on earth is what is known as the Cambrian Explosion. At this point in the fossil record, supposedly 540 million years ago, all of the major body plans of organisms appear quite suddenly. There are no ancestors in the lower rock layers, so it appears as though there were an explosion of evolutionary activity. This would seem to be contrary to the theory of evolution, but

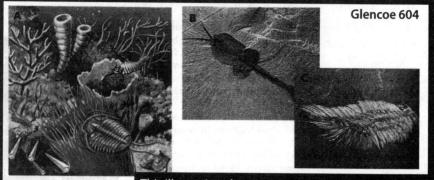

Glencoe 604

Figure 23-5 The Burgess Shale fauna were found in an isolated quarry near the town of Field, British Columbia. The unusual organisms lived a quiet life in the absence of predators **(A)**. *Waptia fieldensis* was an arthropod **(B)**. *Canadia spinosa* was a polychaete or bristle worm **(C)**.

This illustration shows a representation of some of the forms that appeared very suddenly in the fossil record during the period known as the Cambrian Explosion. In the creationist model, these animals represent descendants of the original created kinds that became extinct during the Flood of Genesis. Gradual evolution cannot account for the sudden appearance of so many types of life.

is explained by the presence of alleged dramatic climate changes which led to an increased rate of evolution. The plastic theory of evolution is able to accommodate rapid change or no change at all—the evidence will always support the theory!

Missing from the layers of rock, at any level, are the transitional forms that document how the relatively simple organisms evolved into relatively complex arthropods. When Darwin developed his theory, he expected the fossil record to reveal the missing transitional forms. Over the last 150 years, there has been little in the way of transitional forms revealed. If fish had truly evolved into amphibians over millions of years we would expect to find lots of variations that are partially fish and partially amphibian in the fossil record. There should be a clear line of ancestry from fish to amphibian with countless side-branches of creatures that became extinct. Instead, we find many fish and many amphibians with a few examples of possible transitions.

For example, the recently discovered *Tiktaalik* is hailed as a clear transition by evolutionists. However, this is simply a fish adapted to living in shallow water. Such variety in the fishes is expected when we start from the Bible and consider the creativity of God. Because evolutionists believe fish evolved into amphibians, they interpret *Tiktaalik* as part of that transition. Despite the fact that the ancestors often appear higher in the rock layers than their descendants, the status of transition is claimed.

Have you seen a dinosaur lately? You likely saw one out the window today—as it fluttered by. Birds represent living dinosaurs according to many evolutionists. The theropod dinosaurs grew feathers on their arms and evolved into the many birds we see today. There are those who reject this claim but many dinosaurs are now shown with feathers despite the fact that no fossils with feathers have been found. Those fossils that have feathers have been shown to be frauds or identified as true birds. From a biblical perspective, birds were created before dinosaurs so there is no way to reconcile the evolutionary account with the Bible.

The myth of transitional forms is very evident when we approach the subject of human evolution. Evolutionists would have

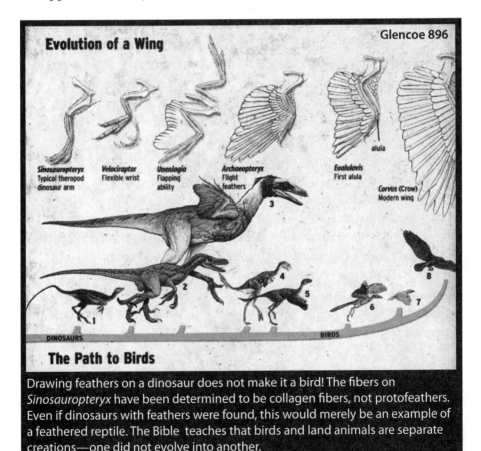

Evolution of a Wing

Glencoe 896

Sinosauropteryx
Typical theropod dinosaur arm

Velociraptor
Flexible wrist

Unenlagia
Flapping ability

Archaeopteryx
Flight feathers

Eoalulavis
First alula

alula

Corvus (Crow)
Modern wing

DINOSAURS

BIRDS

The Path to Birds

Drawing feathers on a dinosaur does not make it a bird! The fibers on *Sinosauropteryx* have been determined to be collagen fibers, not protofeathers. Even if dinosaurs with feathers were found, this would merely be an example of a feathered reptile. The Bible teaches that birds and land animals are separate creations—one did not evolve into another.

When the phrase "human evolution" is used, this is probably one of the first images to pop into people's minds. Despite its iconic status and widespread use, it is not based on factual evidence, but on imagination.

us believe that all apes share a common ancestor. The textbooks present humans arising from this common ancestor over 4 million years ago. Whether this was in Africa or around the world simultaneously has not been determined, let alone which fossil represents the ancestor of modern humans. An examination of the fossils that are proposed as human ancestors, or at least along the branch that led to humans, shows many specimens that overlap in evolutionary time, as well as gaps of millions of years. There is no consensus on the path to humans, and any representation of the lineage is highly subjective. In the biblical creationist model, these specimens either represent some type of extinct ape, or groups of humans.

The moral implications of the evolutionary philosophy that man is simply an advanced ape are increasingly manifested in our culture. If man is an ape, then the apelike or *primal* urges that we have for violence and sexuality can be excused as coming from our evolutionary history. Exercising those urges is contrary to the Christian doctrine of self-control. If we are just advanced apes and ultimately a product of random, cosmic accidents then there is no basis for what is right and wrong. The Bible, on the other hand, provides a clear basis for morality—we are all accountable to the Creator and His moral laws.

Another attempt to cut the Creator out of the picture involves alien life. The search for life on other planets in the universe is based on evolutionary assumptions. According to evolutionists, if life could evolve here on earth then it must have evolved in many different places in the universe. Billions of dollars are spent on determining where and when this life may have evolved. Popular culture reflects this belief in the many different science fiction stories where the alien life offers hope to humanity. Whether this hope is from technology or medical knowledge, these beings are seen as saviors of mankind in many cases. Rather than accepting the Savior revealed in the Bible many people put their hope in something for which there is not a shred of evidence.

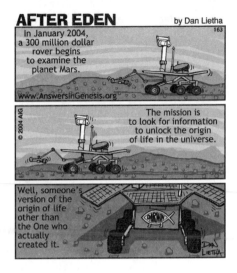

AFTER EDEN by Dan Lietha

In January 2004, a 300 million dollar rover begins to examine the planet Mars.

www.AnswersinGenesis.org

© 2004 AiG

The mission is to look for information to unlock the origin of life in the universe.

Well, someone's version of the origin of life other than the One who actually created it.

The belief in the evolution of life on the earth is simply in total contradiction to what the Bible presents. The fossil record and the observations concerning natural selection do not support the evolutionary worldview unless there is a prior commitment to uphold a belief system. Starting with the truth in God's Word, we must reject evolutionary thinking and the conclusions it leads us to.

Reference Article Summaries

8:1 Is evolution a "fact" of science? Thompson, www.apologeticspress.org/articles/1985

In the media, textbooks, and scientific literature, the occurrence of evolution has become a *fact*. The definition of the word *evolution* has also taken on two different meanings that are not equal. Evolution can be used in the sense of change in a species by natural selection. This is often referred to as microevolution and is accepted by evolutionists and creationists alike as good observational science. This type of evolution allows change within groups but not between groups.

The other meaning of evolution involves the idea that all organisms on earth share a common ancestor by descent with modification. This idea is commonly referred to as macroevolution. [Editors note: AiG does not endorse using the terms *microevolution* and *macroevolution*. It is not the amount of change that is different, but the type and direction of change that is different. These terms do not clarify that difference.] The two definitions are often used interchangeably. Typically, textbooks show that new species can form—evolution has occurred—so they argue that it is obvious that evolution, in the molecules-to-man sense, must have occurred. The problem is that just because natural selection and speciation have occurred (and there is strong evidence to support such claims), the claim that all life has evolved from a common ancestor is based on many assumptions that cannot be ultimately proven.

People believe the ideas of the evolutionary development of life on earth for many reasons: it is all that they have been taught and exposed to, they believe the evidence supports evolution, they do not want to be lumped with people who do not believe in evolution and are often considered to be less intelligent or *backward*, evolution has the stamp of approval from *real* scientists, and evolutionary history allows people to reject the idea of God and legitimize their own immorality. Evaluating the presuppositions behind belief in evolution makes for a much more productive discussion. Two intelligent people can arrive at different conclusions using the same evidence; so their starting assumption is the most important issue in discussing historical science.

When we deal with the issue of origins, we must realize that no people were there to observe and record the events. When scientists discuss the origins of the universe, the earth, or life on earth, we must realize that the discussion is based on assumptions. These fallible assumptions make the conclusions of the discussion less valid than if the discussion were based on actual observation. Almost all biology books and textbooks written in the last two generations have been written as if these presuppositions were true.

Proponents of the evolutionary worldview expect everyone to accept evolution as fact. This is a difficult case to make when the how, why, when, and where of evolutionary history are sharply contested or unknown by the scientists who insist evolution is a fact.

Evolutionists often claim that creation is not scientific because of the unprovable assumptions that it is based on. The fact that evolution is based on its own set of unprovable, untestable, and unfalsifiable assumptions is often unrecognized in the scientific community.

Within the scientific literature, the mathematical and chemical impossibilities of the origin of the universe and life on earth are recognized. Many notable scientists, including Sir Fred Hoyle and Sir Francis Crick, have gone so far as to suggest that life originated on other planets or was brought to earth by an intelligent being. These ideas are no more testable than special creation but avoid invoking God as our Creator.

8:2 Is natural selection the same thing as evolution?

Purdom, www.answersingenesis.org/articles/nab/is-natural-selection-evolution

Natural selection is generally described as the mechanism that is responsible for molecules-to-man evolution. From a creationist perspective, natural selection is a process whereby organisms possessing specific characteristics survive better than others in a given environment. There is no doubt that natural selection can change the genetic make-up of populations, but is that change able to turn one kind of organism into another? Natural selection involves a loss of genetic information and, therefore, cannot be used to explain how all of the life-forms on earth came to be.

The idea of natural selection was first published by Edward Blyth—a creationist. He suggested that God had created the original kinds, and natural selection acted to conserve, rather than originate, new kinds. Darwin popularized the idea of natural selection acting to create new forms of life over time in the absence of God.

Natural selection can be seen as a mechanism that God used to allow organisms to adapt to changing environments in a sin-cursed world. After death entered the world as the penalty for Adam's sin, animals with detrimental genetic changes would be removed from the population and preserve the original kinds. Evolutionists view the history of life as a single branching tree where all life has come from a common ancestor. Creationists view the history of life as an orchard of trees, each representing one created kind. Natural selection allows organisms to adapt to their

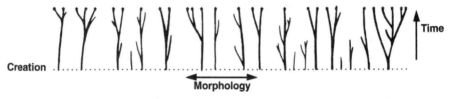

Creation **Morphology** **Time**

Illustration used with permission from Dr. Kurt Wise and Creation Science Fellowship of Pittsburgh from the 1990 ICC Proceedings, Bob Walsh editor, vol. 2, p. 358.

environment, but within the bounds of the kind.

Using dogs as a simplified example, we could start with two dogs that had medium-length fur. Let L represent the long-fur gene and S represent the short-fur gene. By breeding two dogs with genes for medium fur (LS x LS) we could produce dogs with a variety of fur length (SS=short, LS=medium, LL=long). If we placed all of these dogs in a cold environment, the long fur would provide an advantage. If all of the short-fur genes (S) were eliminated from the population by natural selection, this would be an advantage to the population. However, if the climate became warmer then there would be no way (other than a mutation of the L gene) to produce short fur—that information was lost from the population. Natural selection can select for a trait and decrease information, but it cannot provide new traits or information.

A similar example occurs with bacteria and antibiotic resistance. Bacteria can become resistant to antibiotics by losing genetic information or swapping genetic information with other bacteria that have the resistance. Antibiotics generally bind to a protein in the bacterium to block its function, eventually causing the bacterium to die. If there is a mutation in the DNA which causes the protein to have a different shape, the antibiotic cannot bind to it and the bacterium lives. To become resistant, the bacterium has lost the information to make the correctly shaped protein. When it is required to compete with other bacteria in the absence of the antibiotic it is less fit and is eliminated from the population.

Back to the dogs, there was likely one pair of the dog kind aboard the Ark. As they stepped out into the environment, the process of speciation began. In the last 4,300 years natural selection has acted on the genetic variation produced by breeding to produce the different varieties of dogs we see around the world today. However, that variation has only led to different types of dogs, never animals of a different kind. The speciation we observe involves a loss of characteristics and information, not the increase in information required to explain molecules-to-man evolution. Natural selection cannot be the driving force of evolution because it results in a decrease of information.

We have observed the change in dogs over time, but that doesn't mean that evolution has occurred. You can breed wolves to get to chihuahuas, but you can't breed chihuahuas to get wolves—variation in the genetic information has been lost. Darwin used this type of change as evidence without an understanding of the limits of genetic change that are known today.

8:3 Are mutations part of the "engine" of evolution? Hodge, www.answersingenesis.org/articles/wow/are-mutations-the-engine

This article details the common mechanisms of genetic mutation and explains how the mechanisms actually provide examples of a loss of information rather than the creation of new information necessary to explain molecules-to-man evolution. In evolutionary theory, mutations are described as the mechanism that fuels the engine of natural selection, creating new organisms as a result. However, most mutations are either neutral or cause a loss of information in the genetic code of an individual.

Evolution teaches that mutations have accumulated over millions of years to increase the complexity of organisms on the earth. The Bible teaches that, as a result of Adam's sin, all of creation is in a downward slide—including the genetic information that is in every living cell. The law against marrying close relations was not given to Israel until Leviticus 18. Up to this point, the accumulation of genetic mistakes was apparently not significant enough to cause genetic disorders in the offspring of close family members. Today, with thousands of years of accumulated genetic mistakes in the human gene pool, intermarriage would be much more likely to produce children with genetic disorders. So it seems that the explanation of a genetic degradation since the Curse of Adam actually fits the evidence better than the evolution model of increasing complexity.

8:4 Life from life . . . or not? Demick, www.answersingenesis. org/creation/v23/i1/life.asp

Darwin did not directly mention the idea of chemical evolution, but it is a natural extension of the logic of naturalism. Thomas Huxley, known as "Darwin's bulldog," boldly proclaimed the ability of life to come from nonlife. The idea of life coming from nonlife, spontaneous generation, was a popular idea from the time of the Greek philosophers. Louis Pasteur had performed experiments that showed spontaneous generation was not possible; so Huxley called the idea of the origin of life "abiogenesis" and said the evolution of protoplasm from nonliving matter had happened only in the early earth and could no longer be observed. This fact seems to disqualify it from scientific study. From studying the Bible, we should not expect to see life coming from nonliving matter since God ceased His creative activity after Day Six of creation. So, evolutionists accept that spontaneous generation happened to get life started, but it can't happen today—a clearly fallacious argument that is necessary to support evolution.

Scientists tried to show that Pasteur's work was wrong, but the many practical applications of the idea forced scientists to abandon the idea of spontaneous generation. The work of Rudolf Virchow helped to confirm that all cells come from preexisting cells, not chemical imbalances. Still needing a mechanism to create life from matter, Huxley and Ernst Haeckel described a group of organisms between matter and cells. They found what they were looking for (because they had decided beforehand what it would look like), but it was later shown to be a simple mixture of chemicals and seawater. As these men were looking for the origin of life, they had no idea of the complexity of even the simplest cells. Each new discovery at the genetic and molecular level just makes it all the more evident that life did not spontaneously create itself—it had a Creator.

8:5 Can natural processes explain the origin of life? Riddle, www.answersingenesis.org/articles/wow/can-natural-processes-explain

Some evolutionists, realizing the improbability of the spontaneous generation of life, suggest that life started somewhere else in the universe and arrived on earth somehow. The problem with this idea is that it cannot be tested, and it just pushes the problem from earth to another planet. Experiments conducted by Stanley Miller in the early 1950s produced some of the basic building blocks of life, but what conclusions can be drawn from the experiments?

Relying on an intelligently designed procedure and apparatus, Miller succeeded in producing a few of the

20 amino acids found in living things. One of the major problems for the origin of life is the presence of oxygen. Oxygen would tend to destroy the organic compounds needed for life, but if oxygen were absent, the atmosphere would lack an ozone layer to shield the compounds from ultraviolet rays—a Catch-22 for evolutionists. Miller excluded oxygen from his experiment, though today the evidence points to the presence of oxygen in the atmosphere throughout earth's history. Starting in water is also a problem since water tends to break the bonds of some amino acids and prevents them from forming chains. Miller isolated the products in order to avoid this destructive reaction.

Another significant problem is that the amino acids in living things, 20 of the over 2,000 types, are special. Amino acids are found in left- and right-handed forms called enantiomers. Miller's experiment produced a racemic mixture (equal left- and right-handed forms) that is detrimental to life—proteins in living things contain only left-handed amino acids (with few exceptions). No natural process is known that makes only left-handed amino acids. The question now is, "Did Miller's experiments really produce the basic building blocks of life?" Since they produced a mixture of a few amino acids, the answer is clearly "No."

What about information? Every living cell contains a code (A-T, C-G sequence) that originates from a sender (DNA) and is passed to a receiver (RNA) that translates the meaning of the code to produce a protein that is intended to be used by the cell for various functions. If any of the pieces is missing, there is no information, and the cell cannot function properly. Evolutionary hypotheses must be able to explain the origin of this information system and provide a mechanism to increase the amount of information over time. No known natural law can provide a mechanism to accomplish this task. DNA is an amazingly efficient storage device. A one-square-inch chip of DNA could store the information in over 7 billion Bibles—millions of times better than current technology. Biblical creationists have no trouble explaining the presence of such complex information—it was created by the most intelligent Being in the universe.

Evolutionists often claim that, given enough time, evolution was certain to happen. Consider that Bradley and Thaxton calculated the formation of a 100-amino-acid protein assembling by random chance to be 4.9×10^{-191}. It is generally accepted that any event with a probability beyond 1×10^{-50} is impossible, so we must conclude that evolution, requiring thousands of times this amount of complexity, is not likely to occur even if the entire universe were full of organic precursors. Naturalism and materialism can offer no realistic method for the origin of life on earth.

8:6 Round and round we go—proposed evolutionary relationships among archaea, eubacteria, and eukarya, Purdom, www.answersingenesis.org/cec/docs/evolutionary-relationships.asp

In 1977 Carl Woese first identified what he called a third domain of life, named archaea, based on ribosomal RNA (rRNA) sequence comparisons. The other two domains of life are eubacteria (true bacteria, prokaryotes) and eukarya (protists, fungi, plants, animals, and humans). Archaea share some physical characteristics with eubacteria but tend to live in more extreme environments, such as hot springs and high-salt environments. These extreme environments were believed to be present on early earth; hence archaea were thought to be the ancestor to both eubacteria and eukarya. However, further analyses of archaea showed them to be genetically and biochemically quite different from eubacteria, and they are no longer believed to be ancestral to eubacteria.

Archaea are actually more genetically similar to eukaryotes than eubacteria and are often represented as a "sister" to eukarya on evolutionary trees of life. Eukarya have genes that appear to have come from both archaea and eubacteria, and so a genome fusion has been proposed. Archaea have given eukarya their informational genes (genes for transcription, translation, etc.), and eubacteria have given eukarya their operational genes (genes for amino acid biosynthesis, fat biosynthesis, etc.). Rather than an evolutionary "tree" of life, a "ring" of life has been suggested. The archaea and eubacteria (possibly multiple ones) fused using the processes of endosymbiosis and lateral gene transfer to give rise to eukarya.

A subheading in a recent article discussing the challenges of determining evolutionary relationships among these three groups says it well: "More good theories for eukaryotic origins than good data." The scientists are so locked into their evolutionary assumptions that they must keep reinterpreting the data to fit their theories. If they would interpret their data in light of the truth found in the Bible, they would find that the data fits the creation model much better.

God created many individual kinds of archaea, eubacteria, and eukarya. Through the processes of natural selection and speciation, the many different bacterial, plant, and animal species we have today have developed. The common traits seen among these living organisms point to a common designer not a common ancestor.

8:7 What grows on evolution's tree? Morris, www.icr.org/article/577

Evolutionists use the concept of the tree of life to show how all life on earth originated with a single common ancestor. The evidence for the branching tree cannot be found in the fossil record where there are many gaps and reversals. Textbooks present this tree as fact and the evolutionary indoctrination continues. The falsity of the tree is most evident in the "Cambrian Explosion." In these rock layers, the majority of body plans (phyla) appear completely formed without evidence of their ancestry in the layers below. There have been no new phyla since the Cambrian Period when they all appear suddenly. The fossil record stands as a firm testimony to the creation of life, not its evolution by natural processes.

8:8 Gone fishin' for a missing link? Menton and Looy, www.answersingenesis.org/go/tiktaalik

The recent discovery of a fossil fish known as Tiktaalik has caused evolutionists to claim that a transitional form between fish and amphibians has been found. The fossil is claimed to be 375 million years old. With its bony forelimbs and its eyes and nostrils atop a flattened head, it is imagined that it lifted itself with its fins while wading through shallow streams. Several problems are apparent when thinking about calling this fossil a transitional form. The bones in the forelimbs are embedded in the muscle and not attached to the axial skeleton, which is the same bone structure in living fish today. The fossils lack the tail and pelvic fins. The presence of bony fins does not mean that the fish is developing into an amphibian. The coelacanth and lungfish that have been claimed as ancestors to modern amphibians in the past have not lived up to the claims, as this new specimen will not. Basing the interpretation on the flawed evolutionary framework will not lead to a true understanding of organisms that "appear" to be evolving.

8:9 What really happened to the dinosaurs? Ham, www. answersingenesis.org/radio/pdf/whathappenedtodinos.pdf

According to evolutionists, dinosaurs evolved 235 million years ago and dominated the landscape until 65 million years ago when they abruptly and mysteriously died out. According to a biblical perspective, dinosaurs were created on Day 6 of the Creation Week, and most became extinct as a result of the Flood described in Genesis. Not all dinosaurs died in the Flood—they would have been among the many kinds of animals on the Ark. Those that got off the Ark have since become extinct. The history of the dinosaurs is not as complex as evolutionists make it out to be. The different views are a result of starting from a different set of assumptions.

While we don't know everything about dinosaurs, we can draw certain conclusions based on the evidence found in fossils. It is always important to note that what we know about the dinosaurs is limited by the evidence and the amount of interpretation that is reasonable.

The presence of dinosaur/dragon legends suggests that man and dinosaurs lived together. The diet and behavior of

Evolutionists believe that humans and dinosaurs never saw one another because the dinosaurs were extinct millions of years before humans evolved. Creationists claim that dinosaurs and humans were present together before and after the Genesis Flood. Dinosaurs would have been present on the Ark with Noah. After the Flood, dinosaurs apparently were brought to extinction by humans and other pressures. The dinosaur/dragon legends from all over the world support this claim.

dinosaurs can be known before the Fall—they were all vegetarians (see Genesis 1:29–30)—but after the Fall many of them must have become carnivores based on tooth marks on bones in the fossil record. Although we can't know everything about the dinosaurs, if we start with the Bible as the accurate history book of the universe, we can come to many reasonable conclusions about their history.

8:10 Swimming with the dinosaurs, Wise, www.answersingenesis.org/docs2006/0308dinosaurs.asp

A recent fossil find in China lays to rest the notion that mammals were small, nocturnal creatures during the "age of reptiles." An 18-inch creature with a two-layer fur coat, beaver-like tail, webbed feet, and the mouth of a seal was found fossilized in Jurassic Period rock dated at 164 million years old. This find pushes back the arrival of large mammaliaforms by 100 million years. This means that mammal-like ancestors had to evolve fur and other mammalian features on land and then evolve to be able to survive in the sea 100 million years earlier than large mammals were supposed to have evolved. The presence of this mammal-like creature, with all of its unique design features, is not a problem in the creation model because it would have been present on earth immediately after creation. The Flood preserved a sample of organisms that lived with one another from the beginning.

8:11 Does this evolutionary claim have any legs? Wise, www. answersingenesis.org/docs2006/0421legs.asp

A snake fossil found in Argentina has added to the scientific debate over whether snakes evolved on land or sea. The fossil has leg structures where its hind legs should be. The location suggests that snakes evolved on land in the evolutionary story. Whether the "legs" were used for crawling or mating cannot be known from the fossil. Many such "vestigial" structures are supposed to show a transition from legged to legless states. A snake with legs fits within the creation model with no need for adjustments. It is possible that this form of snake had legs, which may have been lost due to natural selection (without demonstrating molecules-to-man evolution).

8:12 The evolution of feathers: a major problem for Darwinism, Bergman, www.answersingenesis.org/tj/v17/i1/feathers. asp

The origin of birds has always been a major problem for Darwinism, and even today little agreement exists about their evolution. One of the most difficult issues related to bird evolution is the evolution of feathers. Feathers are complex, designed structures required for flight, and are today found only on birds. A literature review on the evolution of bird feathers showed that even though feathers are found as far back as the Cretaceous Period, including many well-preserved samples in amber, the fossil record fails to provide solid evidence for feather evolution. The implications of this major difficulty for Darwinism are discussed in this article.

The presence of feathers for flight has allowed birds to spread to every corner of the globe. Their coloration, songs, and flight make them a marvel of God's creation.

Animal skin types range from a thin structure seen in worms to scaly reptiles, feathered birds, and furry mammals. Each of these skin types performs a different function, and the information is different for each type of structure in the skin. Scales, hair, horns, nails, claws, and feathers are all made of the protein keratin and are outgrowths of the skin. Though they are all made of keratin, they are different forms of keratin.

The structure of a feather is much more complex than it appears. Each feather contains a main shaft, barbs, and barbules on the barbs, which contain many small hooklets and grooves that act like Velcro® to hold the feather together. There are over a dozen types of feathers.

The nervous system to control flight is amazingly complex. The complex system of brain, muscles, lungs, tendons, and feathers must have evolved all at once in an irreducibly complex system. Each part by itself would not be likely to provide a survival advantage. The sudden appearance of fully formed feathers in the fossil record supports the idea of special creation. Many evolutionists hypothesize that feathers actually evolved for insulation and were later exploited for flight by modification. Some disagree with this idea, and it is still contested.

The origin of flight in evolutionary hypotheses ranges from tree-down gliders to ground-up flyers. As there is no evidence for either theory, the speculative debate continues. Feathers and bird bones are relatively abundant in the fossil record, with 79% of the 329 living families known from fossils. No transitional structures between scales, skin, and feathers are known from the fossil record, suggesting birds appeared suddenly—during Day Five of Creation Week.

The complex differences between reptilian scales and bird feathers mean that a set of intermediate steps would have been needed, none of which is seen in the fossils. A hair-like follicle must have developed, making the evolutionary connection between hair and feathers more plausible. The problem is that this would not fit the other evolutionary evidence; so a story must be imagined to explain the miraculous development. The development from the billows-style lungs of reptiles to the unique features of the birds' respiratory system is another insurmountable problem for Darwinists. The evidence clearly points to the amazing design of the Divine Creator of the Bible.

8:13 Did dinosaurs turn into birds? Menton, www.answersin-genesis.org/articles/nab/did-dinosaurs-turn-into-birds

Many evolutionists would consider the birds at your bird feeder to be . . . dinosaurs! Far from being extinct, the dinosaurs simply evolved into the birds we see today. The Bible gives a different account. Birds were created "after their kind" on Day Five and then dinosaurs, from which birds allegedly evolved, were created on Day Six. The Bible must have the wrong order if the evolutionary story is true.

Exactly which group of dinosaurs evolved into birds is disputed, but the idea has been popular among evolutionists for over 150 years. The most popular theory today suggests that the theropods, containing *T. rex* and *Deinonychus*, are the ancestors but there are many problems to overcome. Reptiles are cold-blooded, and birds are warm-blooded. Birds would have to evolve highly complex mechanisms to regulate their body temperature. Some argue that dinosaurs were warm-blooded, but there is no convincing evidence for this claim.

All dinosaurs are divided into the lizard-hipped saurischians and the bird-hipped ornithischians based on the structure of the pelvis. Ironically, it is the lizard-hipped theropods that are supposed to have given rise to the birds. A supposed commonality is the three-fingered hand of birds and theropods. Studying the embryological development of fingers has shown that digits 2, 3, and 4 develop in birds while digits 1, 2, and 3 develop in the theropods. If birds evolved form theropods, the same pattern would be expected.

Birds have a unique lung with a one-way air flow design. Reptiles have a billows-style lung where the air entering the lungs mixes with the air exiting. A well-preserved specimen of *Sinosauropteryx* revealed lungs with a diaphragm similar to a crocodile. Theropod lungs are not similar to bird lungs.

Birds are the only living organisms with feathers, and no dinosaurs have been found with feathers. Fossils of *Sinosauropteryx* have been identified with structures called *protofeathers*, but these have been determined to be collagen fibers and bear little resemblance to feathers in the first place. Fossils have been found with scales, but no feathers. In the Chinese fossil beds where the alleged bird ancestors are found, we also find true birds and groups that were once considered feathered dinosaurs but are now conceded to be flightless birds (*Caudipteryx* and *Protarchaeopteryx*). The only theropod fossil *found* with feathers, *Archaeoraptor*, was found to be a fraud after being featured prominently in *National Geographic* in 1999.

Even if a fossilized dinosaur were found with feathers, it would not shake the validity of the Bible, as the Bible does not mention such things. It would simply show design features common between birds and dinosaurs. We see such mosaic features in the platypus. What would be needed to support evolutionary ideas is an intermediate between a scale and a feather. Scales are simply folds of the skin while

The many differences in the development of feathers and scales makes it clear that scales could not have been remodeled to form a feather. Feathers and hair are much more closely related in development.

feathers are formed from a follicle, much like hair, and they have an incredibly complex structure. The vane is divided into rows of barbs, each having hundreds of barbules that interlock with tiny hooks and grooves. There is no similarity, but evolutionists continue to invent stories of how scales evolved into feathers.

Archaeopteryx, considered to be a true bird, occurs in layers dated 20 million years older than its alleged ancestors. The claws, teeth, and long tail are often cited as support for its state as a transition between reptiles and birds. However, ostriches and juvenile hoatzins have fingers, and the extinct *Hesperornis* had teeth.

Regarding flight, there is no consensus on how flight evolved, and flying birds are alleged to occur before flightless birds such as penguins. Theropods have large hind limbs and tails and very small forelimbs—exactly the opposite of what would be ideal for flight. Covering drawings of theropods with feathers will not make them fly.

8:14 Did humans really evolve from apelike creatures?
Menton, www.answersingenesis.org/articles/wow/did-humans-really-evolve

Many popular magazines and television programs show evidence purportedly proving that humans evolved from an apelike ancestor. Is the evidence real, or are they making apes out of men and men out of apes? Starting from biblical assumptions, we see clearly that God made man in His image and did not use evolution. Some Christians who accept evolution say that man's soul was created by God, but evolution made the physical form. The evolutionary assumptions demand that man evolved from an apelike ancestor and discount biblical authority. Paleoanthropologists don't ask *if* man evolved from apes, but *which* apes he evolved from.

The fossil evidence of hominids (alleged human ancestors) is extremely limited, and very few people get to see the actual fossils. Most studies are done from casts of the fossils or pictures. And because jaws and teeth are the most commonly preserved primate fossils, these become a key part of the interpretations. The fraudulent Nebraska Man, including his family and livestock, was identified and drawn based on a single tooth, which was later found to be from an extinct pig.

Skull anatomy is also important, since brain capacity and facial features are used to demonstrate the supposed human-like features in some ape fossils. Leg and hip bones are important in demonstrating how the hominids walked. Those that walked upright are more human than those that didn't.

To make an apelike human ancestor appear out of the fossil record, paleoanthropologists do one of three things. First, they combine pieces from an ape fossil and a human fossil and call it a hominid ancestor. This happened in the case of Piltdown man, which was identified as a hoax after being promoted as man's ancestor for 50 years. The second way is to emphasize the ape features of a human fossil, such as oversized jaws, sloping foreheads, and other features that are found within the range of human variation.

Finally, they emphasize the human features on an ape fossil. This is evident in the fossil "Lucy," an *Australopithecus afarensis* specimen. Even though *A. afarensis* hips don't support the idea that they walked upright and the foot bones are curved like an ape's, it is usually shown standing with human feet—a blatant misrepresentation of the fossil evidence.

8:15 Human Beings, Parker, www.answersingenesis.org/cec/docs/cfl-pdfs.asp

Humans are the result of either a cosmic accident orchestrated by time and chance or the special creative act of God. Evolutionists once viewed Neanderthals as dumb, cave-dwelling brutes that were less than human, but creationists have always argued that they were fully human. Neanderthals lived in very harsh conditions where disease and nutrition may have produced some of the skeletal features seen, and many evolutionists are beginning to accept the creationist view of Neanderthals as an extinct human people group—not a missing link.

Tragically, other human people groups have been considered missing links and treated in barbaric ways. African Negroes and Australian Aborigines were sometimes considered less evolved humans. A century ago, Darwin's idea encouraged the slaughter of Aborigines, and some were even prepared as museum specimens. It also gave credence to Hitler's plan to exterminate the "inferior" Jewish race.

Piltdown man was thought to be a missing link for over 50 years before it was discovered to be a fraudulent combination of a human skull and an orangutan jaw. But because people wanted to believe evolution, they initially accepted the evidence without scientific scrutiny. The many different and dubious interpretations of Java man and Peking man (well documented in *Bones of Contention* by Martin Lubenow) are further evidence that people see what they believe in the fossils. Nebraska man was a hallmark in the Scopes Trial, but the tooth that inspired this image was later determined to be from an extinct pig.

There is no need to look for missing links if man is classified as a monkey, as a 1993 display at the Australian National Museum depicted: the common behaviors in humans and various apes were set forward as evidence for the claim. *Australopithecus*, the genus of the infamous "Lucy" specimen, is one of the most cited examples of a missing link in human evolution. The problem is that australopithecine features are all apelike, despite the claim that they walked upright. Many depictions actually show human hands and feet when the evidence clearly indicates curved, apelike features.

The fact that tools are found with some australopithecine fossils and that human fossils are found in strata directly underneath suggests that the tools may have been used on the apes, not by them. The extinct ape fossils may share characteristics with modern humans, but so do living apes. No evidence from the fossil record directly supports a transitional series from ape to human. Virtually every major discovery is later reinterpreted to fit a new version of evolution. People have always been people and apes have always been apes. Each was created according to the purpose and plan of God.

8:16 Neandertal Man—the changing picture, Oard, www. answersingenesis.org/creation/v25/i4/neandertal.asp

Neanderthals are often portrayed as unintelligent cavemen in animal-skin clothing. Neanderthals were first thought to be subhuman, but that thought is beginning to change. In the creationist view, Neanderthals and Cro-Magnons were post-Flood people groups that resulted after the dispersion from Babel. Neanderthals were originally given the name *Homo neanderthalensis* and considered an ancestor to modern humans. Forty-four years after this biased classification, Neanderthals were reclassified as a human subspecies *Homo sapiens neanderthalensis* and described as nearly human. It has been claimed that they were unintelligent even though their brain capacity was larger than modern humans, and interpretations of their social habits vary from hunter to vegetarian.

The idea that skeletal features of australopithecines are intermediate to humans and chimpanzees is an interpretation that comes from the assumption that chimps and humans have a common ancestor. Starting from a different assumption, that humans and chimps have a common Designer, the evidence points to a Creator using similar structures to perform similar functions.

Neanderthals present a challenge to Christians who believe that soulless humans came before Adam. There is conclusive evidence that Neanderthals and humans lived at the same time. Recent discoveries of a humanlike hyoid bone, burial practices, musical instruments, weapons, and other signs of culture have started to shift the picture in even the evolutionists' minds. Evidence of hybridization between humans and Neanderthals, DNA comparisons, and the indications that they lived together for 100,000 years of evolutionary time point to the fact that they were fully human. This evidence contradicts evolutionary assumptions and supports the biblical position that Neanderthals simply represent some of the variety that was programmed into the human genome by our Creator.

8:17 The Permian extinction: National Geographic comes close to the truth, Silvestru, www.answersingenesis.org/tj/v15/i1/permian.asp

Evolutionists believe that a mass extinction, wiping out 90% of the planet's species, occurred about 250 million years ago. The presence of nine major extinctions has led to much speculation about the cause. Some suggested causes of the Permian extinction are major meteorite impacts, increased volcanism, and depleted oxygen in the oceans. The meteorite impact supposedly caused major dust clouds that led to the collapse of food chains and eventually acute global warming, which wiped out most species. The theory using ocean oxygen levels is unsupported by real evidence. There is a large amount of volcanic activity in Siberia at this point in the strata, and some argue the asteroid evidence is better explained by these volcanoes. The same sort of sun-blocking chain reaction would result from massive volcanic activity.

Creationists explain the apparent mass extinctions as distinct events or zones within the year of the Flood. The idea of asteroid impacts as a trigger for the Catastrophic Plate Tectonics Model developed by Dr. John Baumgardner is an interesting idea. The idea of a lot of small catastrophes over millions of years can all be encapsulated into the 371-day Flood. The evidence for a global flood is misinterpreted by the uniformitarian geologists.

Many people believe that one or more of the major extinction events in evolutionary history occurred as a result of a meteorite hitting the earth. The creation model uses the Genesis Flood to explain the sudden disappearance of the majority of life on earth and the presence of billions of fossils buried in rock layers laid down by water.

8:18 The extinction of the dinosaurs, Oard, www.answersingenesis.org/tj/v11/i2/dinosaur.asp

The disappearance of dinosaurs from the earth in a relatively short time has been a major puzzle for evolutionists. Their wide distribution and adaptation to many climates deepens the mystery. Studying extinctions is difficult because the classification and distribution of species is not well described. Up to nine major extinction events are supposedly preserved in the fossil record, the one at the end of the Cretaceous Period being the most extensive.

Different theories on extinction range from one extreme to the other, including temperature, nutrition, and food supply. Lately, the meteorite extinction theory seems to be the most prevalent. A massive meteorite struck the earth, ejecting debris into the air that cooled the atmosphere. A layer of iridium concentration around the globe, the presence of shocked quartz, and many other types of evidence are supposed support for the theory. The cooling from the debris is alleged to have caused the extinction of the dinosaurs.

A competing theory suggests that the data support a period of massive volcanic activity. Many types of evidence, including the iridium and quartz evidence, are given as support for the theory. The increased volcanic activity would have caused the same cooling effect, as well as releasing toxic gases and killing the dinosaurs. Opponents of each theory have valid arguments to refute one another.

Creationists hold that the destruction of most of the dinosaurs, as well as most other life forms, is accounted for by Noah's Flood. Those dinosaurs that survived the Flood in the Ark have died off since then for various reasons. While there are still many unknowns in the fossil distribution, the presence of massive fossil graveyards, trackways that represent fleeing behavior, quickly deposited layers without channels forming, and other factors clearly point to a flood of global proportions. There are certain aspects of Flood geology that are not entirely understood, but the models are constantly being refined to accommodate these observations. The likelihood of volcanoes and/or meteorite collisions during the Flood explains the evidence for the two most popular secular theories adequately. In total, the Genesis Flood provides a satisfactory explanation for the extinction of a majority of the dinosaurs.

8:19 Did life come from outer space? Grigg, www.answersin-genesis.org/creation/v22/i4/space.asp

The earth seems to have all of the conditions that make life possible. The fact that life evolved so quickly after the earth supposedly cooled from its molten state leads some evolutionists to consider the idea that life originated on another planet. With the billions of stars in the universe, there has to be a planet with earth-like conditions, or so they say. Mars and Europa (a moon of Jupiter) were once thought to have the ability to support life, but the lack of evidence is causing this idea to lose popularity among evolutionists. The attempt to identify planets in distant star systems has produced evidence of such exoplanets, but there are no specific details nor have we directly observed planets outside our solar system.

For rocks to travel from another planet to earth carrying life, or vice versa, the rocks would have to be ejected with the force of a meteor impact, travel for extended periods of time, and be subjected to cosmic radiation. These factors make it highly unlikely that a life form could make the trip. It is remotely possible that there may be bacterial life present on nearby planets if the life was "seeded" from earth. The SETI project, which listens for intelligent signals from outer space, and the recent Mars missions have failed to introduce any evidence. Astrobiology remains a science with no data to support it.

8:20 Are ETs and UFOs real? Lisle, www.answersingenesis.org/
articles/nab/are-ets-and-ufos-real

Science fiction programs depict creatures from distant planets, but many secular scientists believe we will one day discover life on other planets. The Search for Extra-Terrestrial Intelligence (SETI) is scanning the universe with radio telescopes to detect signals from intelligent aliens. Is the idea of alien life biblical?

The idea of extraterrestrial life stems from a belief that the earth is one of the planets where life could have evolved. With billions of planets, life is almost inevitable in an evolutionary worldview. From Scripture, we learn that God created the earth especially to be inhabited and that the other planets have a different purpose. If the alien life were *intelligent* then they could not be redeemed for their sin—they are not descendants of Adam.

The Bible teaches that the first Adam rebelled against God and brought sin and death into the world. The inherited sin problem keeps all humans from being right with God. Christ was the perfect sacrifice, the Last Adam, and has paid the penalty for our sins by taking on human flesh and dying on the Cross. Christ died once for all. If there were human-like beings elsewhere in the universe who were not descended from Adam, Christ could not be the sacrifice for their sins. Some might suggest that Christ lived and died for each of those societies as well, but that is antibiblical as Christ died *once* for *all*.

There is currently no evidence for extraterrestrial life. If it is inevitable that life evolved at many places in the universe, there should be advanced civilizations that evolved billions of years ago. We would expect that these advanced civilizations could have colonized our galaxy. The absence of life in the universe is called the Fermi paradox. What is paradox for evolution is actually a *feature* of the universe described in the Bible. Earth was designed for life and the other planets were not.

Many people have seen unidentifiable objects flying in the sky, but these are just that—Unidentified Flying

Objects. There are many phenomena in the atmosphere and space that can explain these sightings whether or not the individual can explain them or not. How these objects are interpreted depends on the worldview of the observer. From the biblical perspective these cannot be alien spacecraft, and there is no tangible evidence to support such a notion.

So why is our culture so fixated on extraterrestrial life, and why does SETI spend millions of dollars searching for life? Discovering alien life would be seen as a vindication of evolution as it is a prediction of a naturalistic worldview. Some surely hope that aliens may have extensive knowledge to share with us—even the key to living forever. The belief in alien life has become a secular replacement for God. God is the healer of disease and the provider of wisdom and eternal life. The aliens are a way to replace God in this culture.

The first chapter of Romans makes it clear that God has revealed himself through His creation. Many have rejected that message and exchanged the truth for a lie—man's reasoning is set above the knowledge of God. But when we start with the Bible, the evidence is consistent with an earth that is specially created. The magnificent beauty and size of a universe which is apparently devoid of life except for one little world where life abounds, is exactly what we would expect from a biblical worldview.

Questions to Consider

1. Is antibiotic resistance the result of a gain in genetic information or a loss of genetic information?

2. What mechanisms do scientists use to explain how mutations can produce new information to make organisms more complex, when all observed mutations cause a loss of information or no change at all?

3. Can natural selection explain the origin of life on earth?

4. If amino acids in nature come in left- and right-handed forms (enantiomers) how did life evolve to only have left-handed forms?

5. Does the suggestion that chimpanzee and human DNA are similar necessarily mean that they had a common ancestor? Could it also be considered evidence for a common designer?

6. Are there any alternative scientific explanations for humans evolving from apelike creatures?

7. When we look at a car or an airplane, it is only logical to suggest that it was designed with the features that it has. The human body is much more intricate and complex than the most complex machines we can design. Why is it considered illogical to consider that the human body has a designer?

8. It seems that whenever evidence challenges current evolutionary theory, the theory just changes to accept the new data, but the presuppositions don't change. What evidence would scientists accept that would cast doubt on evolution itself?

9. If evolution is not directed by a purpose, would it be safe to say that human existence is purposeless? What is the basis for truth and morality if human life is a by-product of evolutionary processes (random interactions of lifeless chemicals)?

10. If there is absolutely no evidence for alien life in the universe, why are billions of dollars spent to look for it? Isn't this looking for evidence to support a belief?

Tools for Digging Deeper

Bones of Contention by Marvin Lubenow

Creation: Facts of Life by Gary Parker

Darwin on Trial by Phillip Johnson

Darwin's Black Box by Michael Behe

Evolution: A Theory in Crisis by Michael Denton

Evolution: The Fossils Still Say No! by Duane Gish

Evolution Exposed: Biology by Roger Patterson

The Lie: Evolution by Ken Ham

The New Answers Book by Ken Ham et al.

The New Answers Book 2 by Ken Ham et al.

Not by Chance by Lee Spetner

09

PLATE TECTONICS

In the six hundredth year of Noah's life, in the second month, the seventeenth day of the month, on that day all the fountains of the great deep were broken up, and the windows of heaven were opened. And the rain was on the earth forty days and forty nights.

Genesis 7:11–12

What You Will Learn

The motion of the earth's crust is accepted by uniformitarian and creationist scientists alike. The difference lies in the time frame over which the movement has happened. Current seafloor spreading, magnetic reversals recorded in the seafloor crust, similar rocks and fossils across ocean basins, and the puzzle-like fit of continents are evidences that appear to be explainable in slow-and-uniform terms over billions of years. However, these evidences can be better explained by the rapid and catastrophic movement of the plates during the Flood. Computer modeling has shown that the continents could have separated in a matter of weeks—millions of years are not required. The key is the runaway catastrophic rate of sinking of the pre-Flood ocean floor crust after it broke up. Additionally, the catastrophic plate tectonics model provides a mechanism for the rainfall during the Flood and the presence of fossilized marine creatures atop mountains and rock layers spread across the continents. Additionally, the catastrophic plate tectonics model provides a mechanism for the rainfall during the Flood and the presence of fossilized marine creatures atop mountains and spread across the continents.

What Your Textbook Says about Plate Tectonics

Evolutionary Concept	Prentice Hall	Glencoe	Holt	Articles
Plate collisions over millions of years have resulted in the formation of mountain ranges around the world.	9, 332, 372	T420, 440, T441, 444, T522D, 526, 532–534, 546, 606–607, 614–615, 626–627, 638	256, 280–283, T282	9:1
The continents formed gradually over millions of years.	T64D, T251, T278D, 320, T322, 322, 325, 382, T392D	476, 478, 530, T576D, 580, T582, 582–583, 594–595, 605, 607–608, T624C, T626	T237D, 255, 257, 259–300	9:1
The earth's plates move gradually and continuously over billions of years.	10, T246C, 248, 252–254, 271	440, 443–444, 463, T497, T522C–D, 532, 546	T237D, 239	9:1
Magnetic reversals show that the seafloor has been spreading over millions of years.	265–267, 272–273, T392C, 404	450–454, 456	242, 245, 322	9:1
Supercontinents formed and split apart over millions of years.	250, T260, 370, 372–373, 377–379, T379	T442, 444–445, 583, 601–602, 612, T624C, 625, 626, 649	258–259, T259, 698	9:1
Climates have changed as plates have shifted over millions of years.	T124D, T246D, 251	446–447	225, 240, 643	9:1
Hot spots form ocean islands and other features over millions of years.	268, T278C	T470D, 487, 636–638	—	9:1

Note: Page numbers preceded by "T" indicate items from the teacher notes found in the margins of the Teacher's Edition.

What We Really Know about Plate Tectonics

Contrary to what is presented in the textbooks the concept of moving continents was first proposed by Antonio Snider in 1859. Snider started from Genesis 1:9–10:

> Then God said, "Let the waters under the heavens be gathered together into one place, and let the dry land appear"; and it was so. And God called the dry land Earth, and the gathering together of the waters He called Seas. And God saw that it was good.

This passage seems to indicate that all of the land was originally in one place since the seas were in one place. He also used the apparent jigsaw puzzle fit of the continents to support his theory of the movement of the continents during the Flood. His work was not recognized by the scientific community.

The textbooks, and other sources, credit Alfred Wegener for developing the theory of continental drift. Wegener's theory was based on uniformitarian principles and several lines of evidence. He was able to correlate fossils and rock layers across the ocean basins to support his theory. However, the idea was rejected by the scientific community until after his death. There was no known mechanism that could explain how the continents could move through the ocean rocks.

Evidence in favor of the movement of the earth's plates slowly accumulated, and Wegener's theory became widely accepted as it seemed to explain the bulk of the data. The mechanism that Wegener was not able to identify was determined to be the movement of the plates that include not just the continents, but the ocean floor. New ocean floor was created in rift zones along ridges which pushed the old ocean floor down into the mantle under the less dense continental plates. This process of seafloor spreading has been measured, and the current rate of movement of the continents ranges from 1.5–6 inches per year.

Uniformitarian geologists have used this rate and radiometric dating to suggest that the continents were all in one location as supercontinents—800 million years ago in Rodinia and 180 million years ago in Pangaea respectively. Most creation scientists do not disagree with the concept of Rodinia and Pangaea, but the

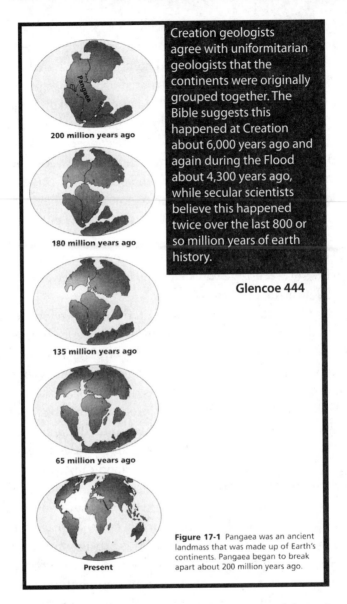

200 million years ago

180 million years ago

135 million years ago

65 million years ago

Present

Creation geologists agree with uniformitarian geologists that the continents were originally grouped together. The Bible suggests this happened at Creation about 6,000 years ago and again during the Flood about 4,300 years ago, while secular scientists believe this happened twice over the last 800 or so million years of earth history.

Glencoe 444

Figure 17-1 Pangaea was an ancient landmass that was made up of Earth's continents. Pangaea began to break apart about 200 million years ago.

timing is another issue. Based on the dates determined from Scripture, the continents were together before and during the Flood about 4,300 years ago. Once again, it is the same set of facts viewed from a different starting point that leads to the interpretations of the past events.

The model now espoused by many creation scientists is called catastrophic plate tectonics and is closely related to the Flood. Rather than the slow continental drift suggested by secular geologists, the biblical explanation can be thought of as continental *sprint*. Rather than acting over millions of years to shape the earth's continents, the originally created continents separated in a matter of weeks, collided, and then separated again during the Flood to arrive at their current positions. This may seem like a radical claim, but computer modeling has demonstrated the feasibility of this model. Dr. John Baumgardner, with the cooperation of others, has used this world-class computer modeling to show how the subduction (sinking into the mantle) of the ocean floor could have happened at a runaway pace. As the region of cold ocean crust near the continents began to sink into the mantle, it pulled the rest of the seafloor with it just like a conveyor belt. New magma rose up replacing the old along what are the mid-ocean ridges today. In just a matter of weeks, the continental plates could have separated and settled near their present positions.

Not only does this model explain the evidence for plate tectonics, it also provides explanations for the processes involved in the Genesis Flood. The Bible speaks of the breaking open of the fountains of the great deep and the opening of the windows of heaven as it rained for 40 days and nights. As the magma rose to replace the spreading seafloor, it would have produced massive jets of steam carrying large amounts of water high into the atmosphere. This matches the description in the Bible and provides a mechanism to explain where all of the water for the Flood came from.

Another effect would be flooding across the continents. As the hot, lower-density magma rose, the new ocean floor would have floated higher than the original ocean crust, displacing the water and forcing it onto the continents. This explains how marine creatures were deposited in thick and extensive layers across the continents and how fossils of marine organisms wound up on the tops of the mountains. As discussed in earlier chapters, the secular uniformitarian model has great difficulty explaining these features.

As the rapidly moving continental plates collided with one another, mountain ranges were produced and forced upward. At the same time, the new seafloor would be cooled and the ocean basins became deeper. The water flowing off the continents would have created massive erosional features and deposited that material onto the continental shelves and the newly formed seafloor.

Despite claims by uniformitarian scientists that the Bible's timeline does not allow for enough time to produce the features we see today, explanations from a biblical perspective make sense of the evidence. It is possible to explain the evidence with models based on biblical truths and within the young-earth timeline of 6,000 years. Conclusions depend on starting assumptions.

Reference Article Summaries

9:1 Can catastrophic plate tectonics explain flood geology?
Snelling, www.answersingenesis.org/articles/nab/catastrophic-plate-tectonics

The study of plate tectonics is an interpretation or model of how the plates of the earth have moved in the past. The earth's crust is made of plates of different types of rock. Continental plates are made of granites and sedimentary rocks and the ocean plates are made of basalt. All of these plates float on the mantle below. Plates can be deformed by rifting, faulting, compressing, and subducting under another plate. Rifting occurs when plates move apart, such as along the Mid-Atlantic Ridge and the East African Rift. Transform faulting happens when plates slide horizontally past one another in places such as along the San Andreas Fault. Compression occurs when plates move toward one another. Ocean plates will plunge below continental plates, but continental plates collide to form mountains like the Himalayas.

In 1859 Antonio Snider used Genesis 1:9–10 and the close fit of western Africa and eastern South America to suggest that a supercontinent split apart catastrophically during the Flood. Over time, the continents moved into their present positions. His theory was unnoticed, and the theory of continental drift was later proposed by Alfred Wegener. His theory was spurned for 50 years by most geologists, and it was called pseudo-scientific fantasy that violated basic principles of physics. Today, plate tectonics involving continental drift is the ruling perspective.

The mapping of the seafloor, measurement of the seafloor's magnetic field directions, radiometric dating, and detection of earthquakes using seismometers all led to an acceptance of the theory. The correlation of fossils across ocean basins, the pattern of seafloor magnetic reversals, and the locations of earthquakes and mountains, along with other evidence, were also elegantly explained by the theory.

Uniformitarian geologists take the vast ages for granted when describing continental drift. Assuming that the rate we see today has been constant, the continents must have been moving for hundreds of millions of years. However, many observations suggest a rapid movement. The seafloor surface appears to have a smooth zebra-striped magnetic pattern, but drilling into the basalts reveals past rapid and erratic changes. This is consistent with the rapid extrusion of the basalts and rapid magnetic reversals during the Flood. The lack of compressional features in ocean trench sediments also points to their rapid deposition at the end of the Flood.

Snider's original proposal of continental sprint, rather than the uniformitarian idea of continental drift, has been supported by computer modeling and explains the evidence better. The catastrophic plate tectonics model begins with a pre-Flood supercontinent, Rodinia. Some sudden trigger cracked the ocean floors next to this cold continent. This caused large blocks to move down into the mantle pulling the ocean floor with them, triggering a runaway subduction event that replaced the entire ocean floor in a matter of weeks. As the crust sank, the mantle rock was displaced and rose along rift zones within the oceans, creating new sea floor.

As this hot magma encountered the ocean waters, great jets of steam were produced, perhaps explaining the "fountains of the great deep" described in Genesis 7:11 and 8:2. This would have caused global rainfall for the duration of the 40 days and nights described in Genesis. The new, hot ocean floor would float higher than the old, cold floor and cause the ocean basins to rise, displacing their waters to flood over the continents. This explains why vast layers of sedimentary rocks containing marine creatures are spread

across the continents, something slow-and-gradual processes cannot explain. The rapid replacement of the ocean
floor would account for the erratic magnetic reversals
recorded in the rocks.

Once the old ocean floor had been subducted, the
process slowed and the new ocean floor rocks cooled. As
they cooled, they would become less dense and sink, allowing the water to flow off of the continents and into the
new deeper ocean basins. The continents would have risen
including the newly formed mountains that resulted from
the collisions of the plates during the Flood. The gradual
rates of current plate movement could not have provided
enough force to create mountains, but the catastrophic collision in a runaway model would rapidly buckle the strata
and push up high mountains.

Plate tectonics is not directly mentioned in the Bible,
but Genesis 1:9–10 suggests that all of the land was once
connected, whereas the continents are now separated. The
catastrophic plate tectonics model and continental sprint
during the Flood can explain this. The model also explains,
in a consistent manner, the global flooding and rain
described in Genesis. Starting with the Bible, an explanation for the global Flood and the movements of the continents can be provided within the biblical time frame—not
billions of years.

Questions to Consider

1. How do slow and gradual processes create enough force to lift
   mountain ranges, such as the Himalayas?

2. Aside from uniformitarian assumptions, is there any reason
   that the continents drifted apart, or could the movement have
   been much faster?

3. How do we know that the rates of plate movement have always
   been similar to the rates of today?

Tools for Digging Deeper

Footprints in the Ash by John Morris and Steve Austin

Grand Canyon: Monument to Catastrophe (Technical) by Steve Austin

The Missoula Flood Controversy (Technical) by Mike Oard

The New Answers Book by Ken Ham et al.

The New Answers Book 2 by Ken Ham et al.

Radioisotopes and the Age of the Earth Volume 1(Technical) by ICR

Radioisotopes and the Age of the Earth Volume 2 (Technical) by ICR

Thousands . . . Not Billions by Don DeYoung

www.answersingenesis.org/go/tectonics

www.answersingenesis.org/go/flood

10

THE ICE AGE

"Although theories abound, no one really knows what causes ice ages."

David Alt, *Glacial Lake Missoula and its Humongous Floods* (Missoula, Montana: Mountain Press Publishing Company, 2001), p. 180.

What You Will Learn

The idea of an ice age has sparked much controversy as well as much imagination. In the framework of an earth that is billions of years old, it is believed that there have been many ice ages. These are believed to have been of different length and intensity, with several covering the entire globe in a *snowball earth* scenario. How life was able to evolve during these periods is not understood, but there are many more problems for the long-age ideas of ice ages. The most significant problem is the explanation of a mechanism that could turn an ice age on and off. Using uniformitarian principles, there is no way to explain, in a consistent manner, how even a single ice age could occur, let alone many over millions of years.

When we start our reasoning from the truth of Scripture, we can develop a model to help us understand the one and only Ice Age. The account of the Flood in Genesis gives us a foundation for a model of this Ice Age. The two key elements for an ice age—a warm ocean and cool continents—are a natural consequence of the Flood, and only the Bible gives us a clear picture of how the Ice Age began and ended. The Bible also helps us to make sense of the presence of mammoths in Siberia and the movement of animals between continents by land bridges. Starting from Scripture, we can better understand the world around us.

What Your Textbook Says about the Ice Age

Evolutionary Concept	Prentice Hall	Glencoe	Holt	Articles
Multiple ice ages have occurred over hundreds of millions of years and caused mass extinctions.	T186C	T165, T369, 370, 610–611, 649	334, 431, 433–434	7:9, 10:1, 10:3, 10:4, 10:5
The last ice age began over 2 million years ago and ended about 10,000 years ago.	188, 198	T52C, T165, 165, T180D, 197–198, 369, 420, T525, 564, 635,	429, 455, T643	10:1, 10:5
The earth was once covered with ice, but most glaciers formed over thousands of years and left behind distinct features.	T186C–D, 188, T464	176, 592, 649	209, 257, 443	10:1, 10:2
Evidence of past climates is recorded in the layers and air bubbles of ice deposits.	T186D	198, 388	209, 434, 641	10:5
Mammals evolved to be large and hairy to survive the last ice age.	T186C	639–640, 566, 572	—	7:9, 10:1
Land bridges allowed people and animals to move between the continents 20,000 years ago.	T186C, T586D	424	455	10:4

Note: Page numbers preceded by "T" indicate items from the teacher notes found in the margins of the Teacher's Edition.

What We Really Know about the Ice Age

Creation scientists and uniformitarian scientists agree that there is strong evidence for a period of extreme glaciation—an ice age—in the recent past. Just how recently is the point of dispute. From a uniformitarian perspective, the earth has experienced many ice ages. Some were so extensive that they almost covered the entire globe in a *snowball earth* scenario. What could have triggered and then ended these events is a mystery to scientists who insist on examining the past based on the processes seen operating in the present. In order to produce an ice age, two ingredients are required: an increase in evaporation causing more precipitation and cold continents on which the snow can accumulate over time. None of the uniformitarian scenarios can produce these conditions.

There is no consensus in the secular scientific community as to what causes ice ages. The most popular models revolve around

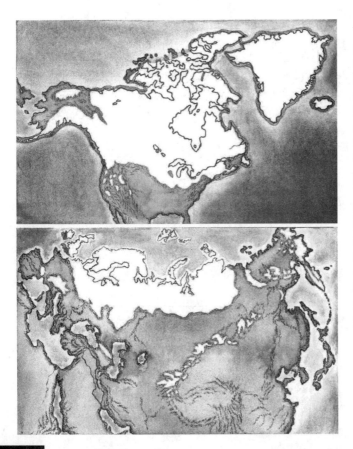

This map shows the extent of the ice sheets over North America during the Ice Age. Scientists who rely on evolutionary thinking believe this was the picture over 10,000 years ago. From a biblical perspective, scientists have suggested the Ice Age was a result of Noah's Flood only a few thousand years ago.

volcanic activity and the changing orbit of the earth around the sun, known as the Milankovitch mechanism. However, neither of these offers a satisfactory explanation. If volcanic activity increased, it would block the incoming light from the sun and cool the atmosphere. Cold air holds less moisture and the amount of precipitation would decrease and prohibit the formation of ice sheets. The Milankovitch mechanism suggests that the atmosphere cooled as the earth moves with respect to the sun in three ways. The earth's orbit goes from a circle to an ellipse in 100,000 year cycles, the tilt of the axis changes over a 41,000 year cycle, and the axis wobbles on a 25,700 year cycle.

These changes are not likely to cause any significant change in the climate and still cannot account for the increased precipitation *and* the cooler continents. Because of the problems with each of the triggers, some scientists suggest that it was a complex interaction of several factors that led to the recurring ice ages. This makes the picture of the past even less clear, and it becomes more difficult to predict the future as well.

To support the multiple ice age theory, uniformitarian scientists have suggested that evidence from shelled organisms on the ocean floor matches the cycles predicted by the Milankovitch model. The direction of coiling changes when the organisms grow in water of different temperatures and the ratio of oxygen isotopes in the shells is supposed to indicate whether the shells grew during periods of glaciation. Because each of these methods starts with the assumption of long ages, they reinforce one another.

So, can the Bible give a clearer picture of the cause of the Ice Age? The answer centers on the Flood and the movement of the earth's crust that accompanied it. As discussed earlier, the Flood likely involved much tectonic activity. This activity provides a mechanism that explains both of the requirements for an Ice Age. As the "fountains of the great deep" broke open, they released heated water and magma. This would have created jets of steam and the rain that accompanied the Flood. The temperature of the oceans would have increased, providing the energy to cause increased evaporation. The increase in evaporation would naturally lead to more precipitation over the continents.

The cooler climate can be explained by an increase in volcanic activity. The volcanism associated with the shifting crust would have released dust and aerosols into the atmosphere. These particles would stay suspended for many years and block the incoming sunlight. The reduced sunlight would cause cooler temperatures over the continents where the increased precipitation would fall as snow and accumulate to form ice sheets. Ice cores reveal volcanic activity extending through the last Ice Age.

With this model, there is a built-in off switch as well. Once the tectonic activity slows to approach the rates we see today, the debris settles out of the air, allowing the continents to gradually warm. The warm oceans continue to lose energy by evaporation until precipitation approaches current rates. This point marks the peak of the Ice Age. Michael Oard, a leading creation scientist with respect to study of the Ice Age, has developed a model that shows this all happening in a period of about 700 years after the Flood. His book *Frozen in Time* details many of the ideas summarized here and ideas found in other technical works regarding the Ice Age.

So, starting from the Bible, we can develop a model that explains the onset and end of the Ice Age. But what about other aspects related to the Ice Age? There is evidence that suggests that climates in various regions around the world were much different during the time of the Ice Age than today. One such region is the Siberian plain. Today this area is frozen for most of the year with little vegetation. The Siberian tundra today would not support the

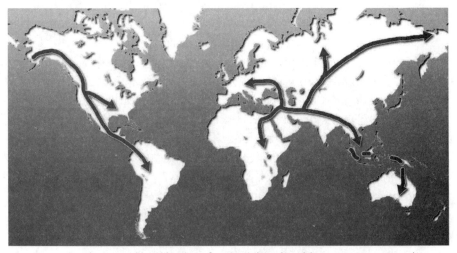

Lower sea levels created land bridges for animals to be able to migrate around the globe. The presence of fossil elephants and camels in the Americas can be explained as a result of the Ice Age.

antelope, beavers, woolly rhinoceros, and woolly mammoths that were present during the Ice Age. To support this large amount of wildlife, the area must have been a lush grassland. This is confirmed by the presence of grasses and flowers in the stomachs of mammoth carcasses—plants that do not grow there today. The area where the mammoths thrived was not covered by ice sheets and must have experienced relatively mild winters to support the diverse population now found as fossils.

The recolonization of animals and plants around the world after the Flood was also accomplished as a result of the Ice Age. As the water evaporated out of the warm oceans and became trapped on the continents as ice sheets, sea level dropped. This created land bridges in the Bering Strait, as well as other places around the globe, allowing animals and people to populate North America during the Ice Age. As the Ice Age ended, these areas filled with water again. Off the northern coast of Siberia, many mammoths were trapped on islands which eventually became their graveyard.

When we begin our attempt at understanding the Ice Age, the Bible gives us a firm foundation. Using the Flood as a part of the explanation, the Ice Age is no longer a mystery, but a natural consequence of the Flood and all of the events that accompanied it. Trying to understand how all of the evidence fits together in the absence of God's Word has puzzled uniformitarian scientists. God has revealed much to us in the Bible, so beginning with that truth as a foundation gives us a much clearer picture than beginning with the reasoning of fallible humans.

Reference Article Summaries

10:1 Where does the Ice Age fit? Oard, www.answersingenesis. org/articles/nab/where-does-ice-age-fit

The idea of an ice age is popular in films, but most people don't look at this idea from a biblical perspective. Despite its popularity in secular circles, there is no good mechanism to explain how a single ice age could occur, let alone the many that have been proposed. The Bible offers a mechanism for the single Ice Age. An ice age is a time of extensive glacial activity, and the Ice Age was a result of the

Scratched bedrock, like this specimen from the Athabasca Glacier in Canada, is evidence of glacial activity.

Genesis Flood. During this post-Flood Ice Age 30% of the land surface was covered with ice. We know the extent of the Ice Age by the physical evidence of moraines, scratched bedrock, and other markers that we see associated with glaciers today.

Uniformitarian scientists believe there have been thirty ice ages over the last several million years. Each ice age coincides with the cycling of earth's orbital geometry. This astronomical explanation for the ice ages is called the Milankovitch mechanism (which has many scientific problems). Each of the last eight ice ages allegedly lasted about 100,000 years and those prior occurred about every 40,000 years. In the distant past, there are supposed to have been four ice ages that were nearly global in scope and lasted much longer. A mechanism that could cool surface temperatures and increase snowfall is absent from the secular models. There are many hypotheses, but no clear explanations.

Uniformitarian scientists reject the Genesis Flood and propose slow and gradual explanations for the volcanic and crustal movements that accompanied the Flood. A shroud of volcanic aerosols would have reflected sunlight back to space, causing cooler summers over land. The Bible tells us that "the fountains of the great deep" burst forth, releasing heated water and lava which added heat to the oceans. The warmer ocean would have increased evaporation and provided moisture to be dropped on the cold continents. This blend of cool continents and warm oceans is the ideal mechanism to create an ice age—a mechanism missing from the uniformitarian model. Using computer modeling, the ice sheets could have formed in less than 500 years.

Most creationists agree that there was one major Ice Age after the Flood. The timing of the Ice Age would have been controlled by the duration of the volcanism and warmer oceans. As the crust settled and the oceans cooled, the Ice Age would reach a maximum about 500 years after the Flood (based on standard heat budget equations), and then the ice sheets would melt over a 200 year period. This would produce catastrophic flooding on a regional scale. Based on biblical assumptions, the Ice Age lasted a total of 700 years—a timescale and mechanism arbitrarily rejected by uniformitarian scientists.

The theory of multiple ice ages is supposedly explained by ice sheets advancing and retreating in cycles during the Ice Age. These ice ages are also based on the assumptions of the Milankovitch mechanism. Ancient ice ages are claimed to have been recorded in the hard rock record, but there are substantial difficulties in interpreting these rocks as coming from ancient ice ages. From a biblical perspective, these can be explained as gigantic underwater landslides during the Flood.

The millions of woolly mammoth fossils found in North America and Siberia are a mystery to uniformitarian scientists. It is likely, from a biblical perspective, that the mammoths populated these areas after the Flood and were then buried during giant dust storms at the end of the

Ice Age. The dust later froze, and the carcasses and bones became trapped in the permafrost.

Another aftereffect of the post-Flood Ice Age was the flooding from glacial Lake Missoula. An ice dam blocked the flow of water in northern Idaho, and a 2,000-foot-deep lake was formed in western Montana. When the dam failed, the water drained and scoured scablands and canyons in eastern Washington and Oregon. This idea was originally rejected by uniformitarian scientists, but is now accepted. This regional flood can help us understand more about the global Flood and the geologic features that are a result of the Flood and the Ice Age.

Uniformitarian scientists claim to be able to count annual layers in the Greenland ice sheet to determine its age in the same way people can count tree rings. In doing so, they arrive at 110,000 years near the bottom of the Greenland ice sheet. Similar claims for a much greater age are made for the Antarctica ice sheet. These claims are essentially based on the uniformitarian belief that the ice sheets are millions of years old. The data from ice cores can be better explained within the post-Flood Ice Age model, which dramatically reduces the calculated age to well within the biblical limit.

Ultimately, the Ice Age as a consequence of the Flood makes better sense of the evidence. From the ice sheet formation to the mammoth fossils and erosional features, starting with the Bible is the key to understanding the past.

10:2 "Snowball Earth"—a problem for the supposed origin of multicellular animals, Oard, www.answersingenesis.org/tj/v16/i1/snowball.asp

Evolutionary scientists suggest that several ice ages that occurred hundreds of millions to billions of years ago actually extended to the equator—the "snowball earth" hypothesis. A major problem is that the snowball condition would be permanent unless there was some catastrophic event to reverse it. Evolutionists face a major problem. Life was supposed to be evolving into multicellular forms at this time—

a difficult task in light of a global ice age. Rock formations also suggest very hot periods immediately after, and sometimes during, these ice ages.

To accommodate this, a freeze-fry model was created that allowed the rapid diversification of multicellular life. Volcanoes penetrated the ice and spewed carbon dioxide into the atmosphere, increasing temperatures via a greenhouse effect. A rapid reversal of temperature provided an opportunity for organisms to diversify. This happened five times in the evolutionary model. These cycles limit the likelihood of evolution occurring even further. There are many other significant problems with the model, and computer simulations have failed to show its viability. Trying to explain the explosion of life at the beginning of the Cambrian Period, while accommodating climate extremes, has proven an impossible puzzle for evolutionists to solve. Creationists can explain the rock evidence in terms of underwater landslides and rock formation during the hot-ocean phase of the Genesis Flood. The abrupt appearance of multicellular organisms is also easily accounted for by their creation and subsequent rapid burial early in the Flood.

10:3 The extinction wars, Oard, www.answersingenesis.org/home/area/fit/chapter5.asp

Some evolutionists believe that at least 30 major ice ages have occurred over earth's history. Most creationists hold to the view that there was a single ice age in the recent past. Evolutionists attempt to show how mass extinctions occurred on a global scale following the last (or first and only) ice age. The explanations include extinction by climate change, extinction by overhunting, or extinction by diseases introduced by humans and their domestic animals. Each of these hypotheses has major problems, and scientists from around the world have been unable to agree on this issue, even after over 100 years of study.

Details within a post-Flood Ice Age model seem to explain the evidence the best, but the Bible is the foundation for such thinking. Therefore, evolutionists must reject the clearest of the interpretations. The problems with the evolutionary model lie in the fact that its basic assumptions do not line up with the true history of the earth described in the Bible.

10:4 How did animals spread all over the world from where the Ark landed? Taylor, www.answersingenesis.org/articles/nab/how-did-animals-spread

Opponents often criticize biblical creationists by suggesting that the worldwide distribution of animals cannot be explained by the Bible. To the contrary, starting from the Bible we can build a model to explain the distribution. From Genesis 6:19–20 we know that representatives of all the kinds of air-breathing land animals and birds were on the Ark. For example, there would not have been two tigers and two lions, but two members of the cat kind from which lions, tigers and other members of the cat kind have developed. These animals were brought to Noah by divine intervention so that the recolonization after the Flood was not left to chance.

We also know from Scripture that the Ark landed in the mountains of Ararat, somewhere in modern eastern Turkey or western Iran. In Genesis 8:15–19 God instructed Noah to bring the animals off the Ark "so that they may abound on the earth, and be fruitful and multiply on the earth." Recolonizing the earth was God's will for the animals.

We can build a model based on these principles. Even if further discoveries were to discredit this model, they would not discredit Scripture. Using the dog kind as an example within the model, we can look at the recolonization. Within a short time period, there would have been many dogs of all different shapes and sizes. These would have begun to spread out and populate new areas, but they were all still dogs. Animals could have crossed oceans or bodies of water on floating log mats, or on land bridges exposed as water evaporated form the oceans during the Ice Age.

Another interesting feature is the association of warm and cold climate animals found as fossils in the same areas in post-Flood sediments. Evolutionists would not expect to find hippos with reindeer, but this can be explained in the biblical model. As these animals were populating new areas with changing climates, some were better able to survive, while others moved to areas where the climate was more suitable for them. Certain populations were better able to survive and colonize certain areas—all within the context of the biblical account of the Flood. Starting from Scripture, we can develop a model that makes sense of the physical evidence that we find across the globe.

10:5 Do ice cores show many thousands of years? Oard, www. answersingenesis.org/home/area/fit/chapter12.asp

Uniformitarian scientists claim that there are 110,000 years recorded in the Greenland ice sheet. The annual layers are clear at the top but become more difficult to define deeper in the ice sheet. The age interpretation is primarily based on the assumption that the ice sheets have existed for millions of years. Slow accumulation over time would allow the lower layers to be compressed to paper–thin layers near the bottom. If the ice built up rapidly, as explained by the creationist Ice Age model, the annual layers would be thick at the bottom, with some compression, and thin toward the top.

Oxygen isotopes are used to determine an "annual signature" for each layer, but the thickness of each layer must be assumed to take the measurements in the correct places. Within the creationist model for the formation of the ice sheets, what is actually being measured is multiple samples within the same year. The layering can instead be explained as storm cycles that mimic annual cycles, and the number of annual layers becomes greatly exaggerated. Likewise, the age of the Antarctic ice sheet is assumed to be 700,000 years old near the bottom. To arrive at this date, an astronomical mechanism for the ice age is assumed to have caused ice ages every 100,000 years. Counting what are assumed to be seven cycles in the ice cores and multiplying by the assumed 100,000 year cycle, a date of 700,000 years is determined.

From the biblical creationist perspective, the Greenland and Antarctic ice sheets are remnants of the Ice Age that followed the Genesis Flood. These ice sheets would have been built up through the Ice Age, which ended about 3,500 years ago, and then slowed as the oceans continued to cool. As evidence of the possibility of rapid growth of the sheets, eight World War II planes were abandoned in Greenland in 1942 and were found in 260 feet of ice in the late 1980s.

The ice cores also show dramatic swings in temperature within very short periods of time, assuming the uniformitarian model is true. This would suggest that dramatic climate changes can occur in decades and fuels the fears of such changes today. If the annual layers are much thicker, these differences would represent annual changes or longer-term changes due to volcanic activity. Again, the Bible offers a clearer way to interpret the evidence.

Questions to Consider

1. What mechanism is used to explain how ice ages begin and end? Have these mechanisms been observed or tested?

2. How are intact mammoth carcasses encased in permafrost explained by scientists?

3. Is the measuring of ice core "dates" an invalid circular argument since the deeper layers are assumed to be many thousands of years older and therefore thinner, which then supports the idea that they are older?

Tools for Digging Deeper

Footprints in the Ash by John Morris and Steve Austin

Frozen in Time by Mike Oard

An Ice Age Caused by the Genesis Flood by Mike Oard

The New Answers Book by Ken Ham et al.

www.answersingenesis.org/go/ice-age

abiogenesis: the alleged spontaneous generation of living organisms from non-living matter

adaptation: a physical trait or behavior due to inherited characteristics that gives an organism the ability to survive in a given environment

anthropic principle: life in our universe requires physical constants, laws, and properties that fall within certain narrow ranges; the universe appears designed to support life

anthropology: systematic study of the characteristics of humans through history

archaebacteria: the kingdom of prokaryotic cells, excluding eubacteria (considered as a separate domain in certain classification schemes), which is alleged to be ancestral to eubacteria by some evolutionists

Archaeopteryx: extinct species of perching bird (known from fossils) with teeth, wing claws, and a bony tail

Archaeoraptor: a fraudulent fossil from China that combined the body of a bird with the tail of a dinosaur

artifact: an item or its remains produced in the past by humans; generally recovered through archaeological exploration

atheism: the belief that God, or any supreme intelligence, does not exist

Australopithecus: genus of extinct apes known from fossils found in Africa, including the famous "Lucy"

bacteria: a group of unicellular organisms that lack a true nucleus and membrane-bound organelles; including eubacteria and archaebacteria

baramin (see created kind)

Bible: the collection of 66 books that is the inspired Word of God; used as the authoritative source for determining truth

biblical creation: the supernatural events, occurring over six approximately 24-hour days, described in Genesis 1 and 2, by which God caused the formation of the heaven and earth and everything in them

biblical creation model: a scientific model based on the biblical account of three key events—creation, the curse of nature brought about by Adam's sin, and the global catastrophe of Noah's Flood

big bang model: the cosmological model suggesting the universe began as a single point which expanded to produce the known universe

biology: the systematic study of the characteristics and interactions of living things

beneficial mutation: a mutation which confers a survival advantage to an organism under certain environmental conditions; usually a result of the loss of genetic information (see mutation)

catastrophism: the doctrine that changes in the geologic record are a result of physical processes operating at rates that are dramatically higher than are observed today

chemistry: the systematic study of the properties and interaction of matter

comet: a body of ice and dirt that orbits the sun as it constantly loses mass

cosmic microwave background (CMB): an invisible source of electromagnetic radiation (microwaves) which seems to be coming from all directions in space; big bang supporters interpret the CMB as radiation left over from the big bang

cosmogony: a belief about the origin of the universe

cosmology: the systematic study of the structure of the universe, including its origin

created kind (baramin): the original organisms (and their descendants) created supernaturally by God as described in Genesis 1; these organisms reproduce only their own kind within the limits of preprogrammed information, but with great variation

Note: Since the original creation, organisms of one kind cannot inter-breed with a different kind, but individuals within a kind may have lost the ability (information) to interbreed due to the effects of the Curse.

Cro-Magnon man: an extinct people group of Europe and Eastern Asia

Darwinism: a belief that all organisms have a single common ancestor that has produced all living organisms through the process of natural selection; popularized by Charles Darwin in *On the Origin of Species*

day-age theory: a compromise belief that the days of Genesis 1 are actually vast ages of different lengths; based on secular dating methods

deism: a belief in a Creator God that denies His intervention in the history of the universe since its creation

DNA (deoxyribonucleic acid): the basic molecule of hereditary information which serves as a code for the production of proteins and is common to all living organisms

endosymbiont hypothesis: the suggestion that mitochondria, chloroplasts, and other organelles originated as bacteria that were ingested and became a part of eukaryotic cells over evolutionary time

entropy (thermodynamics): the measure of the tendency of closed systems to increase in disorder

evolution: all life on earth has come about through descent with modification from a single common ancestor (a hypothetical, primitive single-celled organism)

extrapolation: inferring information outside of the range of the actual data based on trends

faith: belief in things that cannot be directly known or observed

Flood (Noah's Flood): the supernatural event described in Genesis 6–10 that covered the entire earth with water, killing all land-dwelling, air-breathing animals except those aboard the Ark built by Noah

fossil: preserved remains or traces of once-living organisms

   coprolite: fossilized excrement

   included fossils: organisms that are encased in a substance leaving the specimen virtually intact, as in amber

living fossils: living organisms that are virtually identical to fossil organisms; often thought to have been extinct and then discovered

mold and cast fossil: a type of replacement fossil which includes the concave or convex impression of an organism; typical of shells and leaves

permineralized fossil: an organism in which the porous parts are filled with mineral deposits leaving the original superstructure intact

replacement (mineralized) fossil: organism whose entire structure has been replaced by mineral deposits so that none of the original superstructure remains

trace/track/micro fossil: evidence of the activity of an organism, including tracks, burrows, root traces

fossilization: the process of preserving the remains or traces of an organism, generally by some form of petrification

gene: a segment of DNA that codes for the production of polypeptides

gene pool: the collection of varying alleles within a population of organisms

genetics: the study of characteristics inherited by the transmission of DNA from parent to offspring

genome: the complete set of genetic material (DNA) of any cell in an organism

geocentric: using the earth as a central frame of reference

geologic column: the layers of rock that compose the crust of the earth

glacier: a mass of ice formed from compacted snow which is thick enough to flow

half-life: the amount of time required for one-half of the atoms of the parent isotope to decay into the daughter isotope

heliocentric: using the sun as a central frame of reference

heredity: acquiring traits by transfer of genes from parent to offspring

historical (origins) science: interpreting evidence from past events based on a presupposed philosophical point of view

historical theory: an explanation of past events based on the interpretation of evidence that is available in the present

hominid: extinct and living members of the family Hominidae, including modern humans and their ancestors

Homo erectus: fossils of extinct human people groups that are misinterpreted as missing links in human evolution

Homo habilis: an invalid category consisting of various ape and human fossil fragments

homologous structure: any feature that shares a common design with a similar feature in another species of organism (alleged to support common ancestry in evolutionary models)

Homo sapiens: the category that includes modern humans, Neanderthals, and other extinct human groups

human: any member of the species *Homo sapiens*

humanism: a belief in mankind as the measure of all things; based on relative truth and morality and rejecting any supernatural authority

Ice Age: the period of glaciation following Noah's Flood during which a significant portion of the earth had a cold climate

information: an encoded, symbolically represented message conveying expected action and intended purpose

inflation: a variation of the big bang theory in which the universe experiences an acceleraed phase of expansion shortly after the bigg bang

interpolation: inferring information within the range of the actual data based on trends

Java man: the first fossil specimen of *Homo erectus*

Kennewick man: human remains found in Washington State in 1996

kind (see created kind)

life (biological): anything that contains genetic information, can reproduce offspring that resemble itself, grows and develops, controls cellular organization and conditions including metabolism and homeostasis, and responds to its environment

Note: The Bible defines life in a different sense, using the Hebrew phrase *nephesh chayyah,* indicating organisms with a life spirit. Plants are not described as having *nephesh chayyah.*

logic: systematic application of principles of reasoning to arrive at a conclusion

Lucy: a 40% complete fossil specimen of *Australopithecus afarensis* discovered in Ethiopia in 1974 by Donald Johanson

macroevolution: term used by evolutionists to describe the alleged, unobservable change of one kind of organism to another kind by natural selection acting on the accumulation of mutations over vast periods of time

mammal: any organism that has fur and nurses young from mammary glands

materialism: a belief claiming that physical matter is the only or fundamental reality and that all organisms, processes, and phenomena can be explained as manifestations or interactions of matter

metamorphic rocks: rocks that have been altered in texture or composition by heat, pressure, or chemical activity after they initially formed

microevolution: term used by evolutionists to describe relatively small changes in genetic variation that can be observed in populations

mineralization: replacement of material from an object, usually organic, with minerals that harden

mitochondrial DNA (mtDNA): small circular loops of DNA found in the mitochondria of eukaryotic cells

mitochondrial Eve: the most recent common ancestor of humans whose lineage can be traced backward through female ancestors; alleged support for the out-of-Africa hypothesis of human evolution

model: physical, mental, or mathematical representations that can be used to explain observed phenomena and make specific, useful predictions

Mungo man: fossil human remains from Australia dated by evolutionists to 40,000 years or more

mutation: any change in the sequence of DNA base pairs in the genome of an organism

frameshift mutation: addition or deletion of one or more nucleotide pairs in the coding region of a gene causing the triplet codons to be read in the wrong frame

deletion mutation: removal of one or more nucleotide pairs in the DNA sequence

duplication mutation: large segments of DNA that have been copied and inserted into a new position in the DNA sequence, possibly on different chromosomes

insertion mutation: addition of one or more nucleotide pairs in the DNA sequence

inversion mutation: a section of DNA that has been reversed within the chromosome

neutral mutation: any mutation that does not effect the function of an organism

point mutation: addition, deletion, or substitution of a single nucleotide pair in the DNA sequence

translocation mutation: the movement of a section of a chromosome from one position to another, generally between different chromosomes

natural selection: the process by which individuals possessing a set of traits that confer a survival advantage in a given environment tend to leave more offspring on average that survive to reproduce in the next generation

naturalism: a belief denying that an event or object has a supernatural significance; specifically, the doctrine that scientific laws are adequate to account for all phenomena

Neanderthal/Neandertal: an extinct human people group with relatively thick bones and a distinct culture; disease and nutritional deficiency may be responsible for some of the bone characteristics

nebula: interstellar cloud of gas and dust

Nebular Hypothesis: belief that the solar system formed from a spinning, collapsing nebula; the sun formed at the center with the planets forming at various distances.

neo-Darwinism: an extension of Darwinism, which includes modern genetic concepts to explain the origin of all life on earth from a single common ancestor

Noah's Flood (see Flood)

Oort cloud: a hypothetical cloud if icy masses that orbits the sun at a great distance and is the alleged source of long period comets

operational (observational) science: a systematic approach to under-standing that uses observable, testable, repeatable, and falsifiable experi-mentation to understand how nature commonly behaves

operational theory: an explanation of a set of facts based on a broad set of repeatable and testable observations that is generally accepted within a group of scientists

organism: any cell or group of cells that exhibits the properties of life (living things) (see life)

paleontology: the systematic study of the history of life on the earth based on the fossil record

paleomagnetism: record of magnetic field strength and direction recorded in basalts

permineralization: the filling of cavities of an object, usually organic, with minerals, which harden

petrification: processes, including mineralization, permineralization, and inclusion, which change an object, usually organic, into stone or a similar mineral structure

phylogenetic tree: diagrams that show the alleged evolutionary relationships between organisms

Piltdown man: fraudulent "prehuman" fossil consisting of the skull cap of a modern human and the jaw and teeth of an orangutan

plate tectonics: the systematic study of the movement of the plates that make up the earth's crust

> **uniformitarian model (continental drift):** based on the gradual move-ment of the plates over hundreds of millions of years

> **catastrophic model:** based on rapid movement of the plates associated with Noah's Flood

presupposition: a belief that is accepted as true and is foundational to one's worldview

progressive creation: a compromise belief accepting that God has created organisms in a progressive manner over billions of years to accommodate secular dating methods

punctuated equilibrium: an evolutionary model that suggests evolution occurs in rapid spurts rather than by gradual change

radioactive decay: the breakdown of unstable nuclei of atoms releasing energy and subatomic particles

radiometric dating: using ratios of isotopes produced in radioactive decay to calculate an age of the specimen based on assumed rates of decay and other assumptions

> **parent isotope:** original isotope before it has undergone radioactive decay
>
> **daughter isotope:** isotope resulting from radioactive decay
>
> **half-life:** the amount of time required for one-half of the parent atoms to decay into the daughter atoms
>
> **relative dating:** estimating the age of a fossil or rock layer by comparing its position to layers of known age
>
> **absolute dating:** using radiometric dating to test a specimen in an attempt to estimate its age

religion: a cause, principle, or belief system held to with zeal and conviction

RNA (ribonucleic acid): a molecule found in all living things that serves various roles in producing proteins from the coded information in the DNA sequence

secular: not from a religious perspective or source

secular humanism (see humanism)

science: the systematic study of a subject in order to gain information (see also operational science and historical science)

speciation: the process of change in a population that produces distinct populations which rarely naturally interbreed due to geographic isolation or other factors

species: a group of organisms within a genus that naturally reproduce and have fertile offspring

spontaneous generation: the false belief that life can arise from nonliving matter

strata: layers of rock deposited by geologic events

theory (see historical theory and operational theory)

transitions/transitional forms: species that exhibit traits that may be interpreted as intermediate between two kinds of organisms in an evolutionary framework (e.g., an organism with a fish body and amphibian legs)

uniformitarianism: the doctrine that present-day processes acting at similar rates as observed today account for the change evident in the geologic record

vestigial organ: any organ that has a demonstrated reduction and/or loss of function

> **Note:** Vestigial organs include eyes in blind cave-fish but not organs that are assumed to have had a different function in an unknown ancestor.

virus: a nonliving collection of proteins and genetic material that can only reproduce inside of a living cell

Y-chromosome Adam: the most recent common ancestor whose lineage can be traced backwards through male ancestors

The questions indicated below are found at the end of chapters in each textbook and are based on evolutionary concepts or expect answers based on evolutionary ideas. See the introduction for suggestions on how to respond to these questions.

Glencoe Earth Science: Geology, the Environment, and the Universe

Page #	Review Question Number
25	16
263	19
382	13
468–469	1, 3–4, 9, 18, 20, STP1
544	13
574–575	3–5, 8, 11–16, STP 1
598–599	1–2, 4–7, 9, 13–17, 20, 22–26, STP 1, 3, 5
622–623	1–2, 4, 9–11, 15–19, 21, STP 2–4
646–647	7–8, 13–14, 16, 19–20, STP 1–2

Page #	Review Question Number
651	1, 3–5, 7–9, STP 1–2
680	3
709	20
743	9
802–803	8, 21–23
830–831	5, 13, 17, 21–22, 26
856–857	1, 2, 4–6, 13–14, 16–17, 19, 23–25, STP 4
861	UMI 2–3, TC 3

Prentice-Hall Earth Science

Page #	Review Question Number
28–30	2, 3, 9, 11, 36
121	3
275–276	12, 29–30
358–360	1, 3, 5, 10–12, 21–24, 26, 29–31, 33
361	1, 6–7
389–390	1, 3–8, 10–12, 14–15, 17–23, 26–27

Page #	Review Question Number
391	2–5
443	12
499	10
611	1– 5, 7
639	4, 10, 23
669–670	2, 16, 25, 28
725	10, 21, 23

Holt Earth Science

Page #	Review Question Number
19	25–26
176	9–10
202	16, 18–19
204	7–10
228–229	9, 10, 14, 16, 18–19, 23–26, 28–29, 32–33
230–231	1, 6–7, 11–13
262–263	18, 24, 28, 33–34
264	8
366	21
437	32

Page #	Review Question Number
438	7–9
648	8
650	4, 7–9
710–711	17, 19, 24–26, 28–29
712–713	1–3, 5, 12
746–747	5, 10, 16, 22, 25–26
748	9–11
768	4
798–799	2, 3, 11, 17, 21, 25–26, 28, 33–35
800–801	3, 5, 12

INDEX TO GLENCOE EARTH SCIENCE

MYA: million years ago

Contents within parentheses are comments from the author, not concepts described in the textbooks.

Page	Concept	Article Reference
370	Ice ages take place over many thousands of years.	7:9, 10:1, 10:3, 10:4, 10:5
372	The earths orbit changes on a 100,000 year cycle.	3:2, 4:3, 5:2, 5:3
373	The earth's axial tilt cycles every 41,000 years.	3:2, 4:3, 5:2, 5:3
373	The earth's celestial pole switches over 26,000 years.	3:2, 4:3, 5:2, 5:3
385	Since prehistoric times, people have used earth's oceans.	5:1, 5:2, 5:3, 5:4, 5:5, 5:6, 5:7
387	Radioisotope dating indicates that the earth is 4.6 billion years old.	4:1, 4:3, 5:1, 5:2, 5:3, 5:4
387–388	Earth's oceans formed as comets and water vapor collected on the cooling surface of the young, hot earth. Figure 15-3 and 15-4.	3:6, 3:7, 3:8, 3:9, 3:16
388	Volcanoes erupted on the young earth for several hundred million years, and many gases were released into the developing atmosphere.	3:6, 3:7, 3:8, 3:9, 3:16
388	As much as 10% of earth's water has been ice at one point in geologic time.	10:5
393	The salinity of the oceans has changed little over geologic time as fossil shells have the same composition as modern shells. Figure 15-11.	5:1, 9:1
393–395	Salts are added to the oceans at the same rate they are removed, so salinity stays constant. Figure 15-13.	5:1, 9:1
420	The last ice age peaked approximately 10,000 years ago.	10:1, 10:5
424	Land bridges connected continents during the last ice age.	10:4
428	Extinct volcanoes erode within a few million years while underwater volcanoes do not erode.	6:3, 6:5, 6:6, 6:7
429	Seafloor sediments accumulate at the rate of a few millimeters per thousand years.	4:1, 4:3, 5:1, 6:1, 6:2, 6:3, 6:4, 6:5, 6:7, 6:8, 7:11
440	Earth's plates move slowly and cause mountains to form and volcanoes to erupt.	9:1

Page	Concept	Article Reference
590–591	RNA may have been the first reproducing molecule that was an intermediate step in the origin of life based on DNA. RNA cannot be easily synthesized under the conditions of the early earth.	3:7, 8:1, 8:2, 8:4, 8:5, 8:6
591	The oldest fossils are prokaryotes, and eukaryotic fossils are found in 2.1-billion-year-old rocks.	4:1, 4:3, 7:4
591	Life may have begun in hydrothermal vents in the ocean where all of the conditions are present.	3:7, 8:1, 8:2, 8:4, 8:5, 8:6
592	A widespread glaciation occurred 700–800 MYA creating a snowball-earth. Multicellular life evolved after this.	10:1, 10:2
592–593	Ediacaran fossils from 670–570 MYA may be the ancestors to animals of the Cambrian, but many disagree. Figure 22-15.	3:7, 8:2, 8:4, 8:5, 8:6
594–595	Modeling activity of the growth of continents over billions of years.	9:1
596	A Martian meteorite that formed 4.5 billion years ago contains carbonate globules that were mistaken for fossils.	3:7, 8:1, 8:4, 8:19, 8:20
601–602	Laurentia split form Rodinia in the Cambrian and the continents shifted throughout the Paleozoic Era. Figures 23-1 and 23-2.	9:1
604	The Cambrian Explosion had all of the marine groups except one suddenly appearing. Figure 23-5.	8:2, 8:3, 8:7
605	During the Ordovician, North America was at the equator and was covered by seas. Figure 23-6.	9:1
606–607	The Taconic Orogeny built mountains in New York between 480–440 MYA.	9:1
607–608	A series of continental collisions ending in the Mississippian Period produced the remainder of what is North America today. Figure 23-12.	9:1
609	Conodonts are excellent index fossils because they evolved rapidly. Figure 23-13.	6:1, 6:2, 6:3
609	Fossil coral suggests that days were 22 hours, and years were 400 days in the Devonian Period.	7:5, 7:11

Page	Concept	Article Reference
629	Ammonites are excellent index fossils of the Mesozoic Era. Figure 24-5.	6:1, 6:2, 6:3
629	Swimming reptiles ruled the Mesozoic Era oceans. Predatory mosasaurs lived during the Cretaceous Period.	8:2, 8:8, 8:10, 8:11, 8:12, 8:13
629	Flowering plants evolved in the Cretaceous Period.	7:2, 7:3, 8:2
630	Small primitive mammals evolved during the Late Triassic Period.	8:2, 8:10
630	Evolution of the mammalian jaw shown in Figure 24-8.	8:2, 8:10
631	Dinosaurs evolved an upright posture 228 MYA and they ruled the Mesozoic Era land.	8:2, 8:9, 8:12, 8:13
631	Crocodiles and turtles evolved in the Mesozoic Era and survived the extinction of the Mesozoic Era.	8:2, 8:8, 8:10, 8:11, 8:12, 8:13
631	Flying reptiles evolved to dominate the Mesozoic Era. Figure 24-9.	8:2, 8:8, 8:10, 8:11, 8:12, 8:13
632	Birds likely evolved from Saurischia, the "lizard-hipped" dinosaurs.	8:2, 8:9, 8:12, 8:13
633	*Archaeopteryx* was definitely a bird. (Contradicts PH)	8:2, 8:9, 8:12, 8:13
633–634	Volcanoes and a massive meteorite collision in the Yucatan led to a mass extinction 65 MYA at the end of the Cretaceous Period. An iridium layer and other evidence supports this. Figure 24-13.	8:9, 8:17, 8:18
635	The Cenozoic Era has spanned the last 66 million years. Figure 24-14.	4:1, 4:3, 5:1, 6:1, 6:3, 6:5, 7:11
635	The Arctic Ocean began to freeze in the Pliocene Epoch triggering the last ice age.	10:1, 10:5
635	An ice age occurred in the Late Pliocene Epoch through the Pleistocene.	10:1, 10:5
635–636	The Green River formation, which contains 50-million-year-old fossils, was formed as the Rocky Mountains eroded. Figure 24-15.	6:3, 6:5, 6:6, 6:7
636–638	Subduction, hot spots, and plate collisions reshaped North America through the Cenozoic Era. Figures 24-16 and 24-17.	9:1

Page	Concept	Article Reference
657	Sunlight is considered to be a renewable resource because it will continue to be available for at least the next 5 billion years.	3:16
657	Diamonds are replaced over hundreds of millions of years of geologic processes.	5:1, 9:1
662	Banded iron formations may have formed during the Precambrian to form sedimentary rocks.	6:3, 6:5, 6:6, 6:7
664	Burning fossil fuels and forests is believed to play a role in global warming.	1:5
664	Earth's atmosphere was similar to volcanic gases 4.6 billion years ago. Oxygen was released by photosynthesis, and organisms evolved to use oxygen.	3:6, 3:7, 3:8, 3:9, 3:16
679	Fossil fuels are nonrenewable resources that form over millions of years.	5:1, 9:1
686	Fossil fuels are energy resources that formed over geologic time.	7:6, 7:7, 7:8, 7:11
686	All fossil fuels originated from organic matter trapped in sedimentary rock.	7:6, 7:7, 7:8, 7:11
687	Coal formed as plant material slowly accumulated and was buried over long periods of time.	7:6, 7:7, 7:8, 7:11
688–689	Most geologists hypothesize that oil originated organically. Millions of years ago organisms slowly died and were covered by sediments.	7:6, 7:7, 7:8, 7:11
690	Some experts estimate that petroleum resources may be used up within the next 60 years.	7:6, 7:7, 7:8, 7:11
715	Human population growth-curve over 11,000 years. Figure 27-5.	5:1, 5:2, 5:3, 5:4, 5:5, 5:6, 5:7
725–726	Human activity related to carbon dioxide emission is believed to cause global warming, though some scientists disagree.	1:5
740	The early atmosphere had no oxygen until photosynthetic organisms evolved.	3:6, 3:7, 3:8, 3:9, 3:16
740–741	Nonrenewable resources are formed through geologic processes over millions of years.	5:1, 9:1

Page	Concept	Article Reference
741	Fossil fuels formed from organisms that lived millions of years ago.	7:6, 7:7, 7:8, 7:11
741	Natural gas and petroleum formed from accumulations of ancient organic material, primarily plankton, in shallow seas.	7:6, 7:7, 7:8, 7:11
741	Ancient organisms died and settled to the bottom of swamps; their remains partially decayed and formed peat.	7:6, 7:7, 7:8, 7:11
742	Global warming is caused by humans.	1:5
744	Galaxies provide a place for stars to develop, and nebulae provide the materials for stars.	3:1, 3:3, 3:4, 3:5, 3:13, 5:1
755	The entire lunar surface is very old. Radiometric dating of lunar rock indicates an age of 3.8 to 4.6 billion years old. Scientists theorize that the moon was heavily bombarded during its first 800 million years.	3:2, 3:10, 3:11
755	The maria are between 3.1 and 3.8 billion years old.	3:2, 3:10, 3:11
756–757	Several theories of the formation of the moon are given. Despite scientists' uncertainty about how the moon formed, it is important in the sun-earth-moon system.	3:2, 3:10, 3:11
757	Ask students to explain why the moon's surface is a more accurate record of the solar system's history than earth's surface is. The moon's surface reflects conditions and processes that prevailed early in the solar system's history.	3:2, 3:10, 3:11
764	Scientists theorize that earth's gravity slowed the moon until it was in a synchronous rotation.	3:2, 3:10, 3:11
781	Mercury was larger sometime in its geological past.	3:4, 3:5, 3:14
781	Venus's retrograde rotation explained by collision with another object early in the solar system's history.	3:4, 3:5, 3:14
782	Last volcanic eruption on Venus took place about 500 MYA.	3:4, 3:5, 3:14
783	It takes earth's rotational axis about 26,000 years to go through one cycle of precession. Figure 29-11.	5:1, 9:1

INDEX TO PRENTICE HALL EARTH SCIENCE

MYA: million years ago

Contents within parentheses are comments from the author, not concepts described in the textbooks.

Page	Concept	Article Reference
346	Groups of fossils in rock units can be used to determine the relative age of the rock layers.	6:1, 6:2, 6:3
346	Fossils can help determine the complex story of earth's history.	6:1, 6:2, 6:3
347	We know that earth is about 4.5 billion years old, that dinosaurs became extinct about 65 MYA, and the expanse of geologic time is a reality.	4:1, 4:3, 5:1, 5:2, 5:3, 5:4
348	If the half-life and parent/daughter ratio can be measured, the age of the sample can be calculated.	4:1, 4:3, 5:1
348	The rates of decay have been precisely measured and they have been decaying at a constant rate.	4:1, 4:3, 5:1
348	There is no daughter isotope (lead from uranium decay) present when minerals formed.	4:1, 4:3, 5:1
349	Accurate radiometric dates can only be obtained for rocks that have been in a closed system since the rock formed.	4:1, 4:3, 5:1
350	Radiocarbon dating can only be used for dating objects up to 75,000 years.	4:2, 4:3
350	Rocks have been dated to 4 billion years old and meteorites to 4.6 billion years old.	4:1, 4:3, 5:1, 5:2, 5:3, 5:4
351	Tree ring chronologies can help us understand the recent past and overlapping samples can give a longer history.	4:4, 4:5
352–353	The geologic time scale breaks the 4.56-billion-year history of earth into periods and was developed before radiometric dating. Figure 12-17.	4:1, 4:3, 5:1, 6:1, 6:3, 6:5, 7:11
353	Geologic eras and periods are subdivided based on changes in life forms.	4:1, 4:3, 5:1, 6:1, 6:3, 6:5, 7:11
353	The further back in time you go, the less we know from the rock record.	4:1, 4:3, 5:1, 6:1, 6:3, 6:5, 7:11
354	Not all rocks can be dated by radiometric dating, but the geologic time scale has accurate dates.	4:1, 4:3, 5:1, 6:1, 6:3, 6:5, 7:11
354–355	Sedimentary rocks cannot be directly dated, so they are assigned ages based on igneous rocks around them.	4:1, 4:3, 5:1

Page	Concept	Article Reference
380	Reptiles dominated the earth for 160 million years.	8:2, 8:9, 8:12, 8:13
380	Some reptiles evolved flight adaptations just as insects already had.	8:2, 8:9, 8:12, 8:13
380	*Archaeopteryx* was a reptile that led to more successful fliers, the birds. (Contradicts Glencoe)	8:2, 8:9, 8:12, 8:13
380	The dominance of reptiles in the Mesozoic Era was due to the evolution of a shell-covered egg.	8:2, 8:8, 8:10, 8:11, 8:12, 8:13
381	A huge crocodile lived in Africa 110 MYA.	8:2, 8:8, 8:10, 8:11, 8:12, 8:13
381	At the end of the Mesozoic Era many reptile groups became extinct as the result of a meteorite collision.	8:9, 8:17, 8:18
382	The Cenozoic Era encompasses 65 million years and is divided into the 63-million-year Tertiary period and the 2-million-year Quaternary Period.	4:1, 4:3, 5:1, 6:1, 6:3, 6:5, 7:11
382	The geologic record of the Cenozoic Era is more complete than other eras and provides a rich history.	4:1, 4:3, 5:1, 6:1, 6:3, 6:5, 7:11
382	Plate interactions during the Cenozoic Era reshaped North America.	9:1
383	Animals fossilized in the La Brea tar pits roamed the earth from 40,000 to 8,000 years ago.	7:10, 7:11
383	Mammals replaced reptiles and flowering plants dominated the Cenozoic Era.	8:2, 8:10
383	Mammals replaced reptiles at the end of the Mesozoic Era.	8:2, 8:10
383	Mammals evolved live birth, a warm-blooded character, hair, and efficient heart and lungs.	8:2, 8:10
383	The development of flowering plants impacted the evolution of birds and mammals that fed on them.	7:2, 7:3, 8:2
383	The development of grasses led to the evolution of herbivores which led to the evolution of carnivores.	7:2, 7:3, 8:2
384	The many mammals that live today evolved from small primitive mammals.	8:2, 8:10
384	Giant mammals evolved during the Oligocene Epoch but became extinct, possibly due to human hunting.	8:2, 8:10

Page	Concept	Article Reference
385	The extinction of the dinosaurs 65 MYA is strongly linked to a meteorite impact in Mexico, though other theories contradict this idea. Figure 13-16.	8:9, 8:17, 8:18
386–387	Modeling activity of the geologic time scale is presented.	4:1, 4:3, 5:1, 6:1, 6:3, 6:5, 7:11
387	Humans developed in the Quaternary Period.	8:14, 8:15, 8:16
404	Ocean seamounts gradually sink over millions of years.	9:1
408	Abyssal clay forms at the rate of 1 cm per 50,000 years, and the sediment is many kilometers thick in places.	4:1, 4:3, 5:1, 6:1, 6:2, 6:3, 6:4, 6:5, 6:7, 6:8, 7:11
410	Oil and gas form as pressure and heat act on organic material over millions of years.	7:6, 7:7, 7:8, 7:11
423	Large amounts of chemicals were dissolved in the ocean through volcanic eruptions 4 billion years ago.	5:1, 9:1
423	The salinity of the ocean has changed little for millions of years.	5:1, 9:1
477	Earth's atmosphere has changed dramatically over 4.6 billion years.	3:6, 3:7, 3:8, 3:9, 3:16
477	Oxygen began to accumulate in the atmosphere 2.5 billion years ago.	3:7, 8:1, 8:2, 8:4, 8:5, 8:6
494	Photosynthesizing algae added oxygen to the atmosphere starting 3.5 billion years ago.	3:7, 8:1, 8:2, 8:4, 8:5, 8:6
495	The earth's atmosphere began to form 4 billion years ago as volcanoes erupted.	3:6, 3:7, 3:8, 3:9, 3:16
601	Earth's orbit and celestial pole changed over tens of thousands of years.	3:2, 4:3, 5:2, 5:3
602	Natural processes have changed the climate over the 4.6 billion years of earth's history.	5:1, 9:1
602–603	Carbon dioxide emissions are correlated to global warming with no mention of dissenting opinions. (T601 says "many scientists think that global warming is not entirely caused by carbon dioxide emissions.")	1:5
614	Aristotle concluded that the earth was round 2,300 years before Columbus (contradicted on page 11).	1:6

INDEX TO HOLT EARTH SCIENCE

MYA: million years ago

Contents within parentheses are comments from the author, not concepts described in the textbooks.

193–194	By comparing amounts of parent and daughter isotopes in a rock sample, scientists can determine the age of the sample.	4:1, 4:3, 5:1
195	The estimated age of the rock must be correlated to the dating method used (examples of three methods are named in the text).	4:1, 4:3, 5:1
196	Radiocarbon dating is accurate for organic objects up to 70,000 years old. In this way, rock layers can be dated indirectly.	4:2, 4:3
197	Fossils are an important source of information for relative and absolute ages of rocks, and the evolution of living things.	6:1, 6:2, 6:3
197	Fossils of marine organisms found in areas far from any ocean indicate that these areas were once covered by an ocean.	7:5, 7:11
197	Paleontologists unearthed remains of rhinoceroses in Orchard, Nebraska, that are 10 million years old.	7:5, 7:11
198	Only dead organisms that are buried quickly or protected from decay can become fossils.	7:5, 7:9, 7:11
199	Trace fossils can provide information about prehistoric life.	7:10, 7:11
200	Scientists can use index fossils to estimate absolute ages of specific rock layers. Ammonite fossils used to date surrounding rocks to between 180–206 million years. Figure 8-2.	6:1, 6:2, 6:3
208	Geologic map of Ohio showing ages of bedrock layers.	4:1, 4:3, 5:1, 6:1, 6:3, 6:5, 7:11
209	Antarctica may have looked like a Brazilian rainforest 60 million years ago.	10:5
209	Climate in Antarctica has undergone major change over millions of years.	10:5
209	The Antarctic ice sheet formed over a relatively short period (about 50,000 years) approximately 34 million years ago.	10:1, 10:2
210	This illustration shows what one type of dinosaur that lived more than 65 MYA may have looked like.	8:2, 8:9, 8:12, 8:15

211	A geologic column represents a timeline of earth's history.	4:1, 4:3, 5:1, 6:1, 6:3, 6:5, 7:11
211	Many of the fossils discovered in old layers are from species that have been extinct for millions of years.	6:1, 6:2, 6:3
211	No single area on earth contained a record of all geologic time.	4:1, 4:3, 5:1, 6:1, 6:3, 6:5, 7:11
211	Rock layers are distinguished by the kinds of fossils the layers contain. Fossils in the upper, more recent layers resemble modern plants and animals.	6:1, 6:2, 6:3
212	Radiometric dating methods allow scientists to determine the absolute ages of rock layers with more accuracy.	4:1, 4:3, 5:1
212	Scientists can use geologic columns to estimate the age of rock layers that cannot be dated radiometrically.	6:1, 6:2, 6:3
212–213	A unit of geologic time is generally characterized by fossils of a dominant life-form. Each division is defined by the organisms that dominated that time period. Table 9-1.	6:1, 6:2, 6:3
214	The family of modern crocodiles has lived on earth for 65 million years. Figure 3.	8:2, 8:8, 8:10, 8:11, 8:12, 8:13
214	This 4 billion year interval [Precambrian] contains most of earth's history.	4:1, 4:3, 5:1, 6:1, 6:3, 6:5, 7:11
215	Evolution is the gradual development of new organisms from preexisting organisms.	8:1, 8:2, 8:3, 8:4, 8:5
215	Scientists have discovered evidence that species of living things have changed over time.	8:1, 8:2, 8:3, 8:4, 8:5
215	Similar skeletal structures indicate a common ancestor. Figure 1.	8:2, 8:8, 8:10, 8:11, 8:12, 8:13
216	How many MYA did the first unicellular life appear? Figure 9-2.	3:7, 8:2, 8:4, 8:5, 8:6
216	Most scientists agree that earth formed 4.6 billion years ago from a spinning nebula.	3:1, 3:3, 3:4, 3:5, 3:13, 5:1
216	Most scientists agree that the earth formed about 4.6 billion years ago.	4:1, 4:3, 5:1, 5:2, 5:3, 5:4

216	Precambrian time began with the formation of earth and ended about 542 MYA, making up 88% of earth's history.	3:7, 8:1, 8:2, 8:4, 8:5, 8:6
217	Precambrian Period dated to 3.9 billion years.	4:1, 4:3, 5:1, 5:2, 5:3, 5:4
217	Precambrian rocks are extremely old, some dating back nearly 3.9 billion years.	4:1, 4:3, 5:1, 6:1, 6:3, 6:5, 7:11
217	Precambrian shields are the result of several hundred million years of volcanic activity.	4:1, 4:3, 5:1, 5:2, 5:3, 5:4
217	The most common Precambrian fossils are stromatolites.	3:7, 8:2, 8:4, 8:5, 8:6
218	A variety of marine life-forms appeared during the Cambrian Period.	8:2, 8:3, 8:7
219	By the Ordovician Period, vertebrates had appeared.	8:2, 8:8, 8:10, 8:11, 8:12, 8:13
219	Near the end of the Silurian Period, land plants and invertebrates evolved on land.	3:7, 8:1, 8:2, 8:4, 8:5, 8:6
219–220	The first amphibians probably evolved from air-breathing fish called rhipidistians. Fossils indicate that amphibians and reptiles dominated earth in the millions of years after the Paleozoic Era.	8:2, 8:8, 8:10, 8:11, 8:12, 8:13
221	Dinosaurs were wiped out by a meteorite impact at the end of the Mesozoic Era. Figure 9-1.	8:2, 8:9, 8:12, 8:13
221	Mesozoic timeline (Figure 1) shows dinosaurs going extinct due to a meteorite impact.	8:9, 8:17, 8:18
222	A group of dinosaurs raced through a Triassic conifer forest in what is now New Mexico. Figure 9-2.	8:2, 8:9, 8:12, 8:14
222	Ammonites mark Mesozoic layers and occur with the first mammals.	6:1, 6:2, 6:3
223	The impact hypothesis suggests a meteorite impact killed the dinosaurs 65 million years ago.	8:9, 8:17, 8:18
224	Earliest mammals were tiny and rodent-like and appeared in the Mesozoic Era 200 MYA. Great explosion of mammal diversity began 65 MYA.	8:2, 8:10

703	Scientists are excited about the possibility of life on Europa, a moon of Jupiter.	3:7, 8:1, 8:4, 8:19, 8:20
708	The existence of these exoplanets leads some scientists to wonder if life could exist in another solar system.	3:7, 8:1, 8:4, 8:19, 8:20
717	Light has traveled billions of years from its original source. By collecting data, scientists can look back billions of years to find answers to scientific questions about the origin of the universe.	2:1, 2:5
718	Small orbiting objects can provide information about the conditions that existed at the beginnings of our solar system.	3:1, 3:13
720	Most of the moon's craters formed when debris left over from the formation of the solar system struck the moon about 4 billion years ago. Even these younger craters, however, are billions of years old.	3:2, 3:10, 3:11
720	The lava plains on the moon formed more than 3 billion years ago.	3:2, 3:10, 3:11
721	This moon rock is 4.3 to 4.5 billion years old. Figure 28-4.	3:2, 3:10, 3:11
721	Many elements may have boiled off early in the moon's history when the moon was still molten.	3:2, 3:10, 3:11
721	Over billions of years, these meteorites crushed much of the rock on the lunar surface into dust and small fragments.	3:2, 3:10, 3:11
722	The pull of the earth's gravity during the moon's formation caused the crust on the far side of the moon to become thicker than the crust on the near side.	3:2, 3:10, 3:11
723	About 3 billion years ago, the number of small objects in the solar system decreased.	3:1, 3:13
723	Because the moon cooled more than 3 billion years ago, it looks the same today as it did then. Therefore, the moon is a source of information about the early conditions of our solar system.	3:2, 3:10, 3:11
723	The moon formed from an impact and slowly differentiated.	3:2, 3:10, 3:11

INDEX OF ARTICLES BY CHAPTER

Chapter 1: What is Science

Article #	Reference
1:1	Duane Gish, "The Nature of Science and of Theories on Origins," Institute for Creation Research, www.icr.org/article/391.
1:2	Bodie Hodge, "Feedback: A 'More Glorious' Means for Creation?" Answers in Genesis, www.answersingenesis.org/go/glorious.
1:3	Ken Ham, "Creation: Where's the Proof?" Answers in Genesis, www.answersingenesis.org/go/proof.
1:4	Jason Lisle, "God and Natural Law," *Answers*, October–December 2006, pp. 74–78, www.answersingenesis.org /articles/am/v1/n2/God-natural-law.
1:5	Michael Oard, "Human-Caused Global Warming Slight so Far," *Answers*, October–December 2006, pp 24–26, www.answersingenesis.org/articles/am/v1/n2/human-caused-global-warming.
1:6	Danny R. Faulkner, "Creation and the Flat Earth," *Creation Matters* 2 no. 6 (1997), www.creationresearch.org/creation_matters/97/cm9711.html.

Chapter 2: The Big Bang

Article #	Reference
2:1	Ken Ham, ed., *The New Answers Book* (Green Forest, Arkansas: Master Books, 2006) p. 245–254.
2:2	Gary Vaterlaus, ed., *War of the Worldviews* (Green Forest, Arkansas: Master Books, 2005), p. 69–78.
2:3	Donald DeYoung, "New Stars, New Planets?" Institute for Creation Research, www.icr.org/article/403/.

Article #	Reference
2:4	Russell Humphreys, "Our Galaxy is the Centre of the Universe, 'quantized' Red Shifts Show," *TJ* 16 no. 2 (2002): 95–104, www.answersingenesis.org/tj/v16/i2/galaxy.asp.
2:5	Andrew Rigg, "Young Galaxies too old for the Big Bang," *Creation,* June 2004, p. 15, www.answersingenesis.org/creation/v26/i3/galaxies.asp.
2:6	David Coppedge, "The Globular Cluster Bomb," Institute for Creation Research, http://www.icr.org/article/3150/.
2:7	Jason Lisle, "Black Holes: The Evidence of Things Not Seen," *Answers,* January–March 2008, pp. 84–88, www.answersingenesis.org/articles/am/v3/n1/black-holes-evidence.

Chapter 3: Origin of the Solar System

Article #	Reference
3:1	T. Parsons and J. Mackay, "Pierre Simon Laplace: The Nebular Hypothesis," *Creation*, August 1980, pp. 29–32, www.answersingenesis.org/creation/v3/i3/ideas.asp.
3:2	Ron Samec, "The Heavens Declare . . . a Young Solar System," *Answers*, January–March 2008, pp. 30–35, www.answersingenesis.org/articles/am/v3/n1/heavens-declare-young-solar-system.
3:3	Jason Lisle, "First Light From Extrasolar Planets," Answers in Genesis, www.answersingenesis.org/docs2005/0420extrasolar_planets.asp.
3:4	Spike Psarris, "Uranus: The Strange Planet," *Creation*, June 2002, pp. 38–40, www.answersingenesis.org/creation/v24/i3/uranus.asp.
3:5	Spike Psarris, "Neptune: Monument to Creation," *Creation*, December 2002, pp. 20–24, www.answersingenesis.org/creation/v25/i1/neptune.asp.
3:6	Terry Mortenson, "Evolution vs. Creation: The Order of Events Matters!" Answers in Genesis, www.answersingenesis.org/docs2006/0404order.asp.
3:7	Aw Swee-Eng , "The Origin of Life: A Critique of Current Scientific Models," *TJ* 10 no. 3 (1996), www.answersingenesis.org/home/area/magazines/TJ/docs/tjv10n3_origin_life.pdf.

Article #	Reference
3:8	Stephen Austin, "Did the Early Earth Have a Reducing Atmosphere?" Institute for Creation Research, www.icr.org/article/203.
3:9	Frank Sherwin, "Origin of the Oceans," Institute for Creation Research, www.icr.org/article/99/13.
3:10	David Wright, "Lunar Recession: Does it support a Young Universe?" Answers in Genesis, www.answersingenesis.org/home/area/feedback/2006/0811.asp.
3:11	Donald DeYoung, "Have Scientists Discovered the Moon's Origin?" Answers in Genesis, www.answersingenesis.org/Docs/399.asp.
3:12	Carl Froede, "Extraterrestrial Bombardment of the Inner Solar System: A Review with Questions and Comments Based on New Information," *Creation Research Society Quarterly* 38 no. 4 (2002): 209–212, www.creationresearch.org/crsq/notes/38/38_4/Note0203.htm.
3:13	Danny Faulkner, "Comets and the Age of the Solar System," *TJ* 11 no. 3 (1997): 264–273, www.answersingenesis.org/tj/v11/i3/comets.asp.
3:14	Duane Gish, "The Solar System—New Discoveries Produce New Mysteries," Institute of Creation Research, www.icr.org/article/62.
3:15	Andrew Snelling, "Saturn's Rings Short-Lived and Young," *TJ* 11 no. 1 (1997): 1, www.answersingenesis.org/tj/v11/i1/saturn.asp.
3:16	Danny Faulkner, "The Young Faint Sun Paradox and the Age of the Solar System," Institute of Creation Research, www.icr.org/article/429.
3:17	A.J. Monty White, "Proof of Life Evolving in the Universe," Answers in Genesis, www.answersingenesis.org/docs2001/0222news.asp.

Chapter 4: Dating Methods

Article #	Reference
4:1	Ken Ham, ed., *The New Answers Book* (Green Forest, Arkansas: Master Books, 2006), pp. 113–124.
4:2	Ken Ham, ed., *The New Answers Book* (Green Forest, Arkansas: Master Books, 2006), pp. 77–87.

Article #	Reference
4:3	Andrew Snelling, "Radioisotopes and the Age of the Earth," Answers in Genesis, www.answersingenesis.org/articles/am/v2/n4/radioisotopes-earth.
4:4	Frank Lorey, "Tree Rings and Biblical Chronology," Institute for Creation Research, www.icr.org/article/381.
4:5	Michael Oard, "Are There Half a Million Years in the Sediments of Lake Van?" Answers in Genesis, www.answersingenesis.org/articles/am/v2/n2/lake-van-rhythmites.

Chapter 5: Age of the Solar System

Article #	Reference
5:1	Russell Humphreys, "Evidence for a Young World," Answers in Genesis, www.answersingenesis.org/docs/4005.asp.
5:2	Larry Pierce, "The World: Born in 4004 BC?" *Answers*, July–September 2006, pp. 25–27, 72, www.answersingenesis.org/articles/am/v1/n1/world-born-4004-bc.
5:3	Ken Ham, ed., *The New Answers Book* (Green Forest, Arkansas: Master Books, 2006), pp. 25–30.
5:4	Russell Grigg, "Meeting the Ancestors," *Creation*, March 2003, pp. 13–15, www.answersingenesis.org/creation/v25/i2/ancestors.asp.
5:5	Kurt Wise, "Egypt or Babel: Which Came First?" *Answers*, April–June 2008, pp. 30–33,www.answersingenesis.org/articles/am/v3/n2/egypt-or-babel.
5:6	Harold Hunt and Russell Grigg, "The Sixteen Grandsons of Noah," *Creation*, September 1998, pp. 22–25, www.answersingenesis.org/creation/v20/i4/noah.asp.
5:7	"Taking a Bead on an Old Earth," Answers in Genesis, www.answersingenesis.org/articles/am/v3/n1/taking-a-bead.

Chapter 6: Geologic Column

Article #	Reference
6:1	Andrew Snelling, "Geological Conflict," *Creation*, March 2000, pp. 44–47, www.answersingenesis.org/creation/v22/i2/geology.asp.
6:2	Marvin Lubenow, "The Pigs Took it All," *Creation*, June 1995, pp. 36–38, www.answersingenesis.org/creation/v17/i3/pigs.asp.
6:3	Steven Austin, "Ten Misconceptions About the Geologic Column," Institute for Creation Research, www.icr.org/article/242/107/.
6:4	"Focus: Rocks Forming in Months," *Creation*, March 1995, pp.7–9, www.answersingenesis.org/creation/v17/i2/focus.asp.
6:5	Tas Walker, "Grand Canyon Strata Show Geologic Time is Imaginary," *Creation*, December 2002, p. 41, www.answersingenesis.org/creation/v25/i1/grandcanyon.asp.
6:6	John Morris, "A Canyon in Six Days," *Creation*, September 2002, pp. 54–55, www.answersingenesis.org/go/walla-canyon.
6:7	Andrew Snelling, "Uluru and Kata Tjuta: A Testimony to the Flood," *Creation*, March 1998, pp. 36–40, www.answersingenesis.org/creation/v20/i2/uluru.asp.
6:8	John Morris, "How Long Did it Take to Deposit the Geologic Column?" Institute for Creation Research, www.icr.org/article/2478.
6:9	John Baumgardner, "Recent Rapid Uplift of Today's Mountains," Institute for Creation Research, www.icr.org/article/98.
6:10	Robert Doolan, John Mackay, Andrew Snelling, and Allen Hallby, "Limestone Caves: A Result of Noah's Flood?" *Creation*, September 1987, pp. 10–13, www.answersingenesis.org/creation/v9/i4/caves.asp.
6:11	John Morris, "Does Salt Come From Evaporated Seawater?" Institute for Creation Research, www.icr.org/article/532.
6:12	Tas Walker, "Not Ancient Reefs but Catastophic Deposits," *Creation*, December 2002, p. 33, www.answersingenesis.org/creation/v25/i1/catastrophic.asp

Chapter 7: The Fossil Record

Article #	Reference
7:1	David Catchpoole, "Living Fossils Enigma," *Creation*, March 2000, p. 56, www.answersingenesis.org/creation/v22/i2/living_fossil.asp.
7:2	Alexander Williams, "Did Plants Evolve?" *Creation*, September 1997, pp. 10–12, www.answersingenesis.org/creation/v19/i4/plants.asp.
7:3	Alexander Williams, "Kingdom of the Plants: Defying Evolution," *Creation*, December 2001, pp. 46–48, www.answersingenesis.org/creation/v24/i1/plants.asp.
7:4	"Ancient Organisms Stay the Same," *Creation*, June 1999, pp. 7–9, www.answersingenesis.org/creation/v21/i3/news.asp.
7:5	Andrew Snelling, "High and Dry Sea Creatures," *Answers*, January–March 2008, pp. 92–95, www.answersingenesis.org/articles/am/v3/n1/high-dry-sea-creatures.
7:6	Andrew Snelling, "The Origin of Oil," *Answers*, January–March 2007, pp. 74–76, www.answersingenesis.org/articles/am/v2/n1/origin-of-oil.
7:7	John Morris, "The Polystrate Trees and Coal Seams of Joggins Fossil Cliffs," Institute for Creation Research, www.icr.org/article/445.
7:8	John Morris, "Did Modern Coal Seams Form in a Peat Swamp?" Institute for Creation Research, www.icr.org/article/521.
7:9	Michael Oard, *Frozen in Time* (Green Forest, Arkansas: Master Books, 2004), pp. 13–21.
7:10	"Fossils—Do They get More Complex?" *Creation*, March 1998, p. 32, www.answersingenesis.org/creation/v20/i2/fossils.asp.
7:11	Gary Parker, *Creation Facts of Life* (Green Forest, Arkansas: Master Books, 1980), pp. 191–206.

Chapter 8: Biological Evolution

Article #	Reference
8:1	Bert Thompson, "Is Evolution a 'Fact' of Science?" Apologetics Press, www.apologeticspress.org/articles/1985.
8:2	Ken Ham, ed., *The New Answers Book* (Green Forest, Arkansas: Master Books, 2006) pp. 271–282.

Article #	Reference
8:3	Gary Vaterlaus, ed., *War of the Worldviews* (Green Forest, Arkansas: Master Books, 2005) pp. 29–41.
8:4	David Demick, "Life From Life . . . Or Not?" *Creation*, December 2000, pp. 36–41, www.answersingenesis.org/creation/v23/i1/life.asp.
8:5	Gary Vaterlaus, ed., *War of the Worldviews* (Green Forest, Arkansas: Master Books, 2005) pp. 15–28.
8:6	Dr. Georgia Purdom, "Round and Round We Go—Proposed Evolutionary Relationships Among Archaea, Eubacteria, and Eukarya," Answers in Genesis, www.answersingenesis.org/cec/docs/evolutionary-relationships.asp.
8:7	John Morris, "What Grows on Evolution's Tree?" Institute for Creation Research, www.icr.org/article/577.
8:8	David Menton and Mark Looy, "Gone Fishin' for a Missing Link?" Answers in Genesis, www.answersingenesis.org/go/tiktaalik.
8:9	Ken Ham, "What Really Happened to the Dinosaurs?" Answers in Genesis, www.answersingenesis.org/radio/pdf/whathappenedtodinos.pdf.
8:10	Kurt Wise, "Swimming with the Dinosaurs," Answers in Genesis, www.answersingenesis.org/docs2006/0308dinosaurs.asp.
8:11	Kurt Wise, "Does this Evolutionary Claim Have any Legs?" Answers in Genesis, www.answersingenesis.org/docs2006/0421legs.asp.
8:12	Jerry Bergman, "The Evolution of Feathers: A Major Problem for Darwinism," *TJ* 17 no. 1 (2003): 33–41, www.answersingenesis.org/tj/v17/i1/feathers.asp.
8:13	Ken Ham, ed., *The New Answers Book* (Green Forest, Arkansas: Master Books, 2006), pp. 296–305.
8:14	Gary Vaterlaus, ed., *War of the Worldviews* (Green Forest, Arkansas: Master Books, 2005) pp. 43–58.
8:15	Gary Parker, *Creation Facts of Life* (Green Forest, Arkansas: Master Books, 1980), pp. 174–186.
8:16	Mike Oard, "Neandertal Man—The Changing Picture," Answers in Genesis, www.answersingenesis.org/creation/v25/i4/neandertal.asp.

Article #	Reference
8:17	Emil Silvestru, "The Permian Extinction: National Geographic Comes Close to the Truth," *TJ* 15 no. 1 (2001): 6–8, www.answersingenesis.org/tj/v15/i1/permian.asp.
8:18	Mike Oard, "The Extinction of the Dinosaurs," *TJ* 11 no. 2 (1997): 137–154, www.answersingenesis.org/tj/v11/i2/dinosaur.asp.
8:19	Russell Grigg, "Did Life Come from Outer Space?" *Creation*, September 2000, pp. 40–43, www.answersingenesis.org/creation/v22/i4/space.asp.
8:20	Ken Ham, ed., *The New Answers Book* (Green Forest, Arkansas: Master Books, 2006), pp. 237–244.

Chapter 9: Plate Tectonics

Article #	Reference
9:1	Ken Ham, ed., *The New Answers Book* (Green Forest, Arkansas: Master Books, 2006), pp. 186–197.

Chapter 10: The Ice Age

Article #	Reference
10:1	Ken Ham, ed., *The New Answers Book* (Green Forest, Arkansas: Master Books, 2006), pp. 207–219.
10:2	Mike Oard, "'Snowball Earth'—a problem for the supposed origin of multicellular animals," *TJ* 16 no. 1 (2002): 6–9, www.answersingenesis.org/tj/v16/i1/snowball.asp.
10:3	Michael Oard, *Frozen in Time* (Green Forest, Arkansas: Master Books, 2004), pp. 53–60.
10:4	Ken Ham, ed., *The New Answers Book* (Green Forest, Arkansas: Master Books, 2006), pp. 141–148.
10:5	Michael Oard, *Frozen in Time* (Green Forest, Arkansas: Master Books, 2004), pp. 119–126.